They Weren't All Angels

also by Joseph Kessel

THE LION

THE MAGIC TOUCH

THE ENEMY IN THE MOUTH

JOSEPH KESSEL

They Weren't All Angels

Translated by Humphrey Hare

DAVID McKAY COMPANY, INC.

NEW YORK

THEY WEREN'T ALL ANGELS

FIRST AMERICAN PUBLICATION 1965

LIBRARY OF CONGRESS CATALOG CARD NUMBER 65-16905

MANUFACTURED IN THE UNITED STATES OF AMERICA

CONTENTS

INTRODUCTION

THE reader of these reminiscences may well wonder whether a writer who has been neither a soldier of fortune, a professional adventurer, a member of the underworld nor a member of the police, can really have taken part in so many strange and often peculiarly brutal events and had so many companions and friends on the margin of society, of the law, of life and death.

But so it is. I cannot help it. These stories owe nothing to the imagination. I have lived every one of them, even though they do have the fictitious atmosphere of the novel.

In fact, the contrary would have been surprising, when year by year for nearly half a century both by profession and taste I have travelled the world in search of dramatic events and curious characters. Chance, which is always in harmony with one's temperament, has done the rest. Nor are my experiences limited to the reminiscences recorded here.

Why have I selected these particular ones? In fact, there was no question of choice. The chance play of memory operated on its own, merely gathering the scenes which rose of their own accord to the surface.

But was it really chance? We tend too easily to give the name of chance to the secret currents that lie beyond consciousness and have much more power over us than has lucidity. Would the merely fortuitous, a caprice of the shades of the past, have succeeded in linking characters, met at intervals over more than forty years and under many different suns, into a sort of unity in violence and unbridled freedom?

For a long time I thought so. And I thought, too, that I had been attracted to my chance-met heroes by their high relief, their poetry of force and daring.

It was true. But it was only superficially and partly true.

When I think today of the wild Cossacks of the armoured train, of

Moussa, the black killer, of Hippolyte of the penal battalions, of Stiopa, the slayer, and recall myself as I was then, I realise that I resembled them in part of myself. I carried their wild, unbridled instincts in my blood, their frenzied refusal to allow convention, law, measure or limit to affect their desires, pleasures and defiance of destiny. But fear of the policeman and the grip of principles acquired in childhood prevented my going the whole way.

These, my companions of the road, of ports, wars, deserts and taverns, had all the fierce courage of their unbridled desires. Through them, I lived vicariously what I dared not face myself. This was why I sought them out with such ardour and perseverance. This was why they came to me in friendship and complicity, as it were, unveiled.

So, at least, it seems to me.

1

THE TRAIN AT THE WORLD'S END

'I'VE had enough, enough, enough!' the unknown Russian at our table suddenly cried.

For a second his strident, hysterical cry pierced the deafening din of the band and the hubbub of laughter, shouts, calls and boos that filled the huge room.

But no one paid attention to his cry of despair, not even the people who sat near him. He had shrieked like a howling dog and now he hid his face in his hands. They shook with a convulsive trembling.

Only Major Robinson shrugged and said: 'He can't drink. It takes him like that whenever he's had one too many.'

He puffed at his short pipe, which he had seasoned in the Flanders trenches, took a big gulp of the drink he made up himself from vodka, whisky, beer and champagne in certain unvarying proportions, and got to his feet.

'That's done it, Major, you're damned drunk,' Bob Lorène, a fellow-officer from my squadron, remarked with a laugh.

'I'm never drunk, young man,' Robinson replied with an austere and melancholy dignity. 'I merely want to have a bit of fun.'

As he spoke he took off his jacket and unbuckled his belt. His trousers followed, then his shirt. Major Robinson was now dressed in short underpants and uniform cap. He made his way through the drinkers and climbed on to the stage, which at that moment was empty.

'Music!' he ordered the shaggy pianist, whom nothing could surprise.

The chords of a prehistoric waltz rang out. Major Robinson danced a cake-walk.

'Bravo!' Bob Lorène shouted.

He beat time by breaking the plates and glasses that had accumulated in front of us.

Harry, who was sitting next to me, said sententiously: 'We must quiet these drunks down.' He was a captain of American Marines, recently arrived from Manilla. 'Yes, we must quiet them down.'

He took a big Colt from the holster that dragged at his belt and fired it at the ceiling.

Pieces of plaster fell. There was a deafening clamour from all over the room.

'Outside! Turn the fools out!' some were shouting.

'No, no!' others protested. 'Let them amuse themselves if they want to.'

Everyone was yelling at everyone, shouting in every language in the world: French, Russian, English, Roumanian, Polish, German, Hungarian, Czech. And the din was sustained by the drumming of boots on the floor, the clatter of breaking glasses, the clinking of spurs and the banging of revolver butts on the tables. Riot hung on a gesture, by a thread.

Suddenly there was silence. Faces changed expression. Quarrels were forgotten. Weapons no longer threatened. All eyes turned in the same direction, towards the stage.

A dozen half-naked girls had appeared. The dozen girls of The Aquarium.

In February 1919, The Aquarium was the only nightclub that counted in Vladivostok. I have never met, in nearly fifty years of travelling from country to country and continent to continent, a more nocturnal spot. By this I mean that it opened its doors only at two o'clock in the morning. And since the Siberian night is very long in winter, The Aquarium's customers had plenty of time before them till sunrise.

The customers were from every part of the world; they were officers of every rank, corps and army. What were they doing in this town beside the Pacific, which the Czars had built at the end of the longest railway line man had ever laid, so that it might be, as it were, a window on to the great Ocean? No one knew. Of the French flying and tank officers, the commanders of the Polish, Roumanian, Hungarian and Czech legions formed from liberated prisoners, the American Marine officers, the commanders of the kilted Scottish, the turbaned Sikhs and the Canadians in short fur jackets, none knew the precise reason for his presence here on the threshold of an immeasurable, limitless land, subject to deep snow, murderous cold, civil war, typhus and hunger.

Kolchak still figured at this time as a leader in Siberia. But the Reds had already crossed the Urals. Bolshevik partisans patrolled the white plains and the dark forests. Cossacks, owing obedience to no one, ruled on Lake Baïkal. Elsewhere, escaped or liberated convicts had organised their own bands. The eager, disciplined Czech troops formed a world apart. And the Japanese, who kept out of every disturbance and every alliance, quietly and patiently pursued their own mysterious affairs.

Somewhere in the infinite expanses of snow, fighting was going on amid unspeakable confusion and chaos. Refugees were pouring into the town in their thousands; but the town could not deal with them and simply let them die—there is no other word for it—regardless. Revolution snarled in the alleyways of the port, contained merely by the fear inspired by the warships of all the nations, tall grey steel ghosts caught in the wan ice.

The troops, thrown into Vladivostok by the whim of the staffs or of destiny, waited unoccupied for the situation to be resolved, and for their respective countries to decide either to bring them home or send them into battle. They waited in cold and sordid makeshift barracks, among a hostile, starving population at the end of the world.

And the officers, who were drawing double pay, came to spend it in the only possible place, The Aquarium.

They had come out of war. They were mostly under thirty. Many of them had scarcely reached their majority. Idleness and the influence of this most sinister of towns were completing their nervous confusion. Over there, so far away that it made them giddy to think of it, post-war life was starting on its mad dance in Paris, London and New York. They had nothing but The Aquarium, its infernal drinks—and its girls.

But there were only twelve of them for a hundred young men—men as starved of sensuality as they were of tenderness. Twelve robust, luxuriant creatures, wholly suited to the fatigues of the night and adulterated liquor. The time had not yet come when poverty and despair, the most hopeless and pathetic destitution, cast delicate and refined young girls into the sailors' bars. Those of The Aquarium had been born to their trade and did not suffer from it.

But the law of supply and demand was peculiarly weighted in their favour. They could pick and choose, and did so. Money no longer sufficed to seduce them. We all had some. We were all prepared to place our pay at the feet of these buxom sirens who made up our feminine world. And this enabled them to make much greater demands than are usual among women of easy virtue. They were athirst for homage. Unconsciously perhaps, they sought some compensation for their condition, for the brutal treatment they must have suffered during the vagabond life they had led in bars and nightclubs throughout the immensity of Russia. And our carnal desires and our hunger for sentiment were so powerful that these prostitutes aroused in hardened, unbridled, uprooted and nearly always drunken young men a spirit of competition in polite attentions and delicate compliments.

That Russian was my mother's tongue gave me an advantage over my competitors. This and the fact that I wore a French uniform, decorated with wings on the jacket collar, endued me with a sort of double, ambiguous and disconcerting personality which found favour with The Aquarium dancers. It was rare that one of them did not honour my table with her presence. I think, too, that they liked being able to talk easily with a man who had, nevertheless, the prestige of a foreigner. For in this unhappy town the Russians were looked on as pariahs. This always happens when a nation is torn in two and has to summon 'saviours' to its aid.

However that may be, on this particular night one of The Aquarium girls joined us. Her name was Marfa. She was quite good-looking, with thick, chestnut, peasant hair, burnt-hazel eyes and a healthy, sturdy body. I immediately made sure my cap was on straight. Bob had the broken plates and glasses removed, Harry blushed and replaced his Colt in its holster and Major Robinson dressed with the speed of a conjurer. Only the unknown Russian gave no sign. He kept his face hidden in his hands and continued to weep. But we were used to his crazy behaviour. It was the third night he had come to our table, begun by talking brilliantly, telling stories of every capital in Europe—expressing himself perfectly both in French and English—drunk a dozen glasses of chemical brandy and sunk into despair.

He went on like this till I left Vladivostok. I never discovered who he was or what he did.

Marfa's presence stimulated our vanity. We each wanted to buy a bottle of champagne. Not that it was good, but it was very expensive. The girl seemed flattered. And we drank till dawn, that's to say till nine o'clock in the morning.

This was my usual time to leave The Aquarium to go on duty, which consisted in overseeing the loading of the trains that supplied the Annamite infantry who, by some ridiculous decision, had been sent to Omsk, one of the coldest places in the world.

'Where are you going?' Marfa asked, when she saw me get to my feet.

'To the station.'

She hesitated a few seconds and then also got up.

'I'll come with you,' she said. 'I think my Cossack will have arrived.'

We got into a sleigh. The filthy coachman, whose great-coat shone with dirt and frost, whipped up his horse. The morning was dark and dirty and the dim light the colour of mud.

'My God,' Marfa cried, hurriedly and fearfully crossing herself. 'My God, what's all this?'

We had entered the hall of Vladivostok station.

At first, I did not understand my companion's horrified surprise. I had been crossing the place every morning for a fortnight on my way to my duty. And since, throughout that fortnight, I had regularly come direct from The Aquarium, chronic lack of sleep and the anaesthesia of alcohol, added to custom, had made me insensible—or nearly so—to the sight that impressed Marfa so much.

'Wait, wait,' she murmured, 'my head's swimming.'

She was clutching at the sleeve of my overcoat and her fur-lined cork shoes were against my boots. She seemed incapable of taking a step forward.

'Are you feeling ill?' I asked. 'Too much champagne?'

'Are you utterly heartless?' Marfa cried. 'Doesn't the sight of all this misery affect you?'

'Have you never been here before?' I asked. It was my turn to be surprised.

'How on earth should I?' she went on irritably, as if her ignorance were my fault. 'I stay at The Aquarium till nine or ten in the morning, then I go off with a man. I sleep all day, dress at midnight, and then go back to The Aquarium. No, I've never been here before.'

She shivered, and looked about her with wide, staring, bewildered eyes. And as a result of her emotion, as often happens, my own eyes were stripped of the film of habit and saw the spectacle before them as if for the first time.

Indeed, there was enough to shake nerves less hardened than mine to disaster, destitution and the most sordid abjectness.

It was quite simple: in February 1919, the hall of Vladivostok station resembled a human dust-bin. Old people of both sexes, abandoned children, Chinese without a roof over their heads, vagrants—everyone who, in this town of poverty, famine, disorder and foreign domination, had neither lodging nor food—had made their way to this asylum which no one now attempted to control. There was not an inch of space to spare on the benches or even on the ground. Entangled bodies, twisted by the cold; ragged Chinese with pale faces in which the lustrous eyes looked like tears in suspense; little children's hands blue under the dirt; the coughing of consumptives; the smell of a sick, ill-kept herd, shut up for days and nights in the same byre.... And on every face the same expression of passive, abject distress, of destitution and accepted defeat.

I thought for a moment of the hall I had just left, where the vulgar music was still playing, and officers half-crazed with drink and lust continued to destroy themselves in a sort of delirium. In spite of my twenty years and the ignorant, superficial view of life that was then mine, I was ashamed of them, of myself and of the whole human race.

'Come on,' I said abruptly to Marfa.

Stepping over the supine bodies, sometimes treading on them, we reached the platform. With what delight I filled my lungs with the damp, heavy air of that dark and joyless morning. It seemed to me a wonderfully pure elixir.

Marfa sighed deeply and crossed herself. There was no longer any trace in her expression of the bright arrogance she assumed every night in The Aquarium. She had become a humble, timid little peasant girl again.

'Where's Ataman Semenoff's train?' Marfa asked a surly, slovenly railway official.

'To hell with the lot of them, the sons of . . .' he began. But he saw my uniform and badges of rank, and muttered as he went off: 'I know nothing about it.'

'The stationmaster will tell us,' I said to Marfa.

The stationmaster had the rank of colonel in the Czar's old army. He had kept it in Kolchak's army. I knew him well. My duties brought me into daily contact with him, since the Siberian adventure had transformed me from a pilot into a loader of trains.

For the purpose, I had at my disposal a gang of raw, underfed Chinese coolies, a Czech sergeant of peculiar energy and intelligence, and limitless funds in roubles with which to buy wagons, locomotives, food, equipment and drivers—at that time everything in Vladivostok was for sale.

The Russian colonel was not of much use to me, but I saw him with pleasure because of his courtesy which, in that inferno, seemed prehistoric.

As we were about to enter his office, I heard Marfa whisper with mingled rapture and dread: 'Look, look . . . There he is. How handsome he is . . . And how terrible . . . I love him.'

The man Marfa indicated had just emerged from a passage. He was wearing Cossack uniform. He had his back to us, but one could readily understand how the girl from The Aquarium had recognised him without seeing his face. The proud shoulders, the narrow waist, the high, defiant carriage of the head and the animal suppleness of his whole body were sufficient to identify him.

'I knew him in Omsk,' Marfa went on, talking to herself rather than to me. 'A long time ago. I lived with him for a fortnight. I can't forget him . . . He is . . .'

A muttering of fear drowned the girl's impassioned whispering.

The stationmaster's office was always overflowing with a singular and varied crowd: distracted officials, bewildered by the lack of equipment, the chaos and the orders issued by twenty different authorities; passengers without trains; the victims of thieves; women who had lost their children; and representatives from various headquarters awaiting or dispatching convoys. Throughout the day this crowd importuned Colonel Lavroff, to whom had fallen the unenviable command of Vladivostok station.

Just as Marfa was advancing, as if fascinated, towards the man whose features I had not yet seen, the whole pitiful human herd retreated towards us with a gasp of horror.

The Cossack was suddenly standing alone in the centre of the huge room. I saw that he had raised his whip above his head. It consisted of a cruel thong of thick leather attached to a short handle, a weapon rather than a whip.

'Look out. Look out. Take care!' frightened voices called.

Others whispered in panic, 'He's one of Semenoff's officers.'

'Silence!' the Cossack shouted.

He had only turned for a second, but it had been long enough for me to make out his thin mouth in which cruelty was allied to a strange despair. Framed by a fur cap and a great-coat criss-crossed with bandoliers, his face stood out in striking relief.

'Silence!' the Cossack ordered.

And everyone fell quiet.

'Who's in command here?' he asked, his whip still threatening.

A clerk moved timidly out of the crowd against the wall and said, 'The Colonel's not here.'

'Go and get him.'

'But...'

'Are you answering me back, you son of a bitch?'

There was a whistle. A sound of tearing flesh. The howl of a beast. The thong had fallen across the clerk's face and had opened his cheek. The blood spurted.

There was a cry from the crowd in which indignation and fear were mingled. The Cossack glanced round, his eyes looked slightly crazy and his nostrils were dilated. There was an immediate and profound silence.

It was suddenly broken by a voice I knew well. It was Colonel Lavroff's, trembling with suppressed shame.

'Lieutenant,' he began, 'I am informed. What does this mean?'

The Cossack gave him no time to finish.

'Here you are at last,' he said. 'Get me some candles. And hurry up about it.'

'I forbid you... I forbid you to talk to me like that... I'm your superior officer. It's... it's...'

Lavroff was stammering. His face was the same colour as his grey hair.

'Superior officer,' the Cossack laughed. 'I'll show you . . .'

The brown thong whistled again, biting savagely into the old face. It was too much. I advanced on the Cossack, my hand on my revolver. My wrist was caught in a strong grasp. I turned round furiously. The Czech sergeant, who was my second-in-command and whom I liked very much, was restraining me with deference, but also with firmness.

'Sir,' he said, 'allow me to remind you of the order.'

He was right. We had strict orders not to interfere in quarrels between Russians, no matter what the circumstances.

But someone had had the same reflex as I, though for a different reason. It was Marfa. The barbarous brutality of her former lover had so fascinated her that she was acting in a state of semi-consciousness.

She presented her fresh, plump face to the whip which was still quivering in the Cossack's upraised hand.

'Hit me, hit me!' she wailed. 'I'm dying to talk to you.'

The Cossack hesitated a moment, and then began laughing.

'Marfouchka,' he said. 'That's very funny.'

His face assumed an unbelievably childish expression.

'Are you alone?' he asked.

'Yes . . . No . . . I mean . . .' she stammered.

I went up to them.

'Oh, a French officer!' the Cossack said. I was not sure precisely what his exclamation implied.

He looked me up and down, and then smiled good-humouredly. Was his friendliness due to the fact that we were the same age and held the same rank? Or was it due to the strange confidence which adventurers, the worst and the best, have placed in me in every country in the world? I do not know. But the Cossack said suddenly: 'Come and have a drink, both of you.'

I hesitated for a moment.

'Is everything all right with the Chinese?' I asked the Czech sergeant.

'There are no difficulties with the loading this morning, sir,' he replied.

'Well, I'll leave things to you then.'

We set off towards the platform. The crowd made way for the Cossack. When he reached the door, he shouted without even turning round, 'Send me the candles, or I'll come back with some men and then there'll be real trouble.'

Then he turned to me very politely and said, 'I'll go ahead. You don't know the way.'

It was not a way I was ever to forget.

Of the surroundings of the station's central building I knew only the enclosure in which my work took place. It was there I joined each morning my fifty ragged, shivering, skeleton-like Chinese coolies, led by their contractor, a fat man in a wadded robe who was the only one of them who understood Russian. Till evening, I superintended these miserable human ants, impatiently awaiting the hour when I could go to wash, change and exorcise with a good deal of alcohol the crushing fatigue accumulated during sleepless nights and joyless days.

There was, therefore, much that was new to me during this unexpected walk on which I was being taken by Semenoff's lieutenant of Cossacks, who had suddenly taken a liking to me, after disfiguring two men out of sheer caprice.

I could not forget those faces convulsed with pain and pouring blood. And I could not take my eyes off the terrible whip which was swinging in the Cossack's hand to the uneven rhythm of our steps.

Snow had fallen all night, but the frost had come only with the morning. As a result, the thin surface often cracked under our weight and we sank up to our thighs. Where the half-solid, half-liquid surface held, it was appallingly slippery.

We had the alternative of walking with unstable balance along the rails. But one soon twisted one's ankles at that game and we had to resume the snowy, icy path.

Léonide Savine—the Cossack had introduced himself as we walked—did not seem particularly inconvenienced by these obstacles. He had the agility of those men who are like animals in their supple movements and the quick, light response of their muscles. In spite of my youth, I was less comfortable. I was wearing leather boots, whereas Savine was shod with *valenki*, those felt boots the Russian peasant dons with the first snow.

As for Marfa, the walk was torture to her. The buxom girl from The Aquarium stumbled at every step. Her confined night-life, drink, smoke, dancing and the noise of the establishment in which she reigned were no preparation for this matutinal adventure over frozen rails, drifts and mounds.

She dropped a long way behind us.

Savine paid no attention to her. He walked on, never turning, as sure of her fidelity as of a devoted dog's.

We had been walking for a quarter of an hour. The station building had disappeared. And we were still following the rails which crossed and mingled with each other like interminable, leaden snakes.

'Where are we going?' I asked at last.

'To my place, as I told you,' Savine, who had not so far said a word, replied briefly.

In spite of his obvious ill-temper, I persisted, 'I can't see a house, or a . . .'

'I haven't lived in a house for over a year,' the Cossack interrupted.

'Well then . . .'

'Don't worry. My lodging's as good as a palace. But it's rather far away.'

Savine swore with appalling obscenity and went on, 'Those blasted clerks, those damned officials . . . One day we shall be the masters here, as we are at Chita. Then, we'll see.'

He suddenly seized me by the wrist and cried, 'If you foreigners didn't protect them, the Ataman would have put paid to them long ago.'

Then he shrugged and said: 'Forgive me. You're already my guest and I oughtn't to . . . But when I see it, it makes me mad.'

We had turned into a siding and suddenly the rails were full. Grouped in twos and threes, or indeed whole rows, there were goods wagons all round us. Savine pointed to the first wagon with his whip. The thong quivered to his anger.

'I don't understand,' I said.

'It's because of these damned refugees,' Savine cried, 'that we have to break our legs to reach the town.'

'I still don't understand,' I said.

'It's clear enough,' he muttered.

He went over to the wagon and gave the door a smart blow with the handle of his whip. There was no answer, and after a few seconds he opened the sliding doors himself. He had scarcely done so when he leaped back muttering, 'Oh, the bastards . . .'

I also moved back. A horrible stench, a sort of foetid miasma floated out to us. In spite of the repugnance which shrivelled my nerves, I forced myself to take a few steps towards the open doors and look inside. This is what I saw:

The wagon had a stove—which was out—in the middle of it and the pipe went out through a hole in the corner, immediately under the roof. Round the stove and the pipe planks had been fixed to the walls one above the other. They were covered with rags or rotten palliasses. And on these pallets lay, in twos or threes, heaps that I had to call human since I could find no other name for them. There were men, women and children. None of them moved. Some were already dead. Others muttered incomprehensible words. But putrefaction was gaining even on those who were clinging to their last breath.

'Typhus . . .' Savine said.

'But . . . but,' I muttered, 'are all the other wagons full too?'

'I hate to say it,' said the Cossack. 'Sometimes ten thousand arrive from European Russia or from Siberia and no one knows where to put them. So they're left here to die . . .'

'What, have they all got typhus?'

'You can be sure they all have in this train. The contagion's very rapid. As for the others, whether it's some other disease, or hunger, they'll die too. So, I ask you, as man to man, wouldn't it have been better to set fire to the whole lot long ago?'

He spat in disgust and concluded, 'And place our train nearer the station?'

While I was thinking about these trains that had been made into habitations and cemeteries and imagining with horror the fate of hundreds of thousands of men and women driven by the revolution towards Vladivostok, the terminus of the Trans-Siberian and the fatal goal of the exodus, which so far only the advance-guard of the refugees had reached, we attained at last the objective to which Léonide Savine was leading us.

By us. I really mean Savine and I. Marfa, caught in a drift or having sprained her ankle, had been lost on the way.

But how could I be expected to remember her when confronted with a sight that had both something of the machine age and something of the dark ages?

In a loop of the deserted railway repair siding stood a line of coaches that bore no resemblance to those of the miserable refugees I had seen a few moments before. They made up one of those splendid trains which, in the old days of peace, carried passengers from Moscow to the Pacific across the plains, forests, mountains and huge lakes of Siberia. Its mere size and appearance spelt comfort, space and luxury. And under the tragic February sky, so low and leaden that it seemed a tangible menace, among the coiling viperine rails leading to the mysterious horizon, close to the convoys which typhus was peopling with corpses, one might have thought that this luxury train had come from another world.

But what world? Why were there men wearing bandoliers and carrying rifles at every door and on every step? What were these wild figures in fur caps doing? And why, beside the locomotive with steam up, were the driver and fireman being watched by guards with pitiless eyes? I asked Savine and added, 'After all, you're not in enemy territory?'

He shrugged violently and gave a mirthless laugh.

'For us,' he said, 'for the Ataman's men, there is no such thing as friendly or enemy territory. There's only conquered territory. And we set up our tents everywhere at our peril.'

Savine went up to the leading coach. The sentries saluted. But though they addressed him as 'your honour,' as under the *ancien régime*, there was less of discipline in their voices and attitude than of complicity.

As soon as I had climbed up into the train, I saw the reason for this singular understanding. Things spoke for themselves. It was as if I had been suddenly transported to some fabulous pirates' lair.

The doors of the compartments were open and they were overflowing with the most extraordinary loot. Valuable weapons and wonderful furs hung from the walls or had been thrown haphazardly on the seats. Bokhara rugs were strewn about the floor, muddied by boots and torn by spurs. Splendid stuffs covered the tables. Massive silver cups and gilt plates lay about everywhere. It was evident that the men who travelled in this strange buccaneer craft of the snows and the civil war were not to be looked on as a military formation but as a gang.

At the same time, I realised that the stories I had heard at The Aquarium about Ataman Semenoff and his men were true. Until now I had thought them the product of over-excited imaginations.

The stories ran as follows:

While the Bolsheviks were trying to conquer and overthrow the whole immensity of Russia, while in Siberia their opponents were fighting internecine battles and Admiral Kolchak was seizing a more nominal than real power, a non-commissioned officer of the Trans-baïkal Cossacks, with a following of only eleven horsemen, began a war on his own account.

They were brave and pitiless. On the shores of the great Lake Baïkal, they surprised and massacred the red partisan bands. Their audacity and success attracted volunteers. Deserters, adventurers, students, bandits and escaped convicts—in fact, anyone who wanted a violent and orgiastic life—came to join Semenoff. They were all true Cossacks and he appointed himself their ataman.

The widespread chaos was in their favour. They seized villages and then towns. Finally, they took Chita, a vital position on the Trans-Siberian. Then, like the leader of a band in the Middle Ages, Semenoff imposed a feudal toll on all trains. Nothing passed through Chita—food, gold, arms or munitions—without his taking his share. As for his men, he abandoned the countryside to them. Their share was pillage, forays, massacre, battle and rape. The life these wild partisans led made them a little more callous each day.

What was Léonide Savine's detachment doing in Vladivostok? I never knew. Perhaps the Cossacks did not know themselves, even their officers. It is impossible to describe the folly and delirium then existing in that part of the world.

Savine had a private compartment. It was there he treated me as an honoured guest. So much so, indeed, that I confess my memory of the sequence of events is somewhat confused. We began with vodka. It must have been nearly 80 per cent. proof.

Savine then introduced me to two young officers. They were very like him in the audacity and cruelty of their features. With them, we drank brandy.

Then the train-commander arrived. He was a man of about fifty and had the look of a convict. I believe, indeed, that he had been one in the Altai mines. He had just got up. He drank a mixture of vodka, brandy and champagne. So did we.

This man had an appalling voice, coarsened by bad tobacco and strong spirits, but he played the guitar divinely. The sounds he drew from the strings had an intolerable naïvety and sadness. They were prison laments.

I remember the commander regretted not having chosen Baron Ungern-Sternberg for leader instead of Semenoff. He had just conquered Mongolia and the Ourga tribes called him 'the Buddha of the Sword.'

I remember, too, how one of those present told how he had nailed the bodies of peasants to posts along the road in such a way that their right arms were raised and all pointed in the same direction, to Semenoff's headquarters. When the frost had seized on the bodies, they had become so many sign-posts leading to the Ataman's outposts.

This story had the immediate effect of dissipating the drunken euphoria in which I was sunk.

'Forgive me,' I said, 'it's nearly noon. I must go back to my duties.'

This aroused a good deal of amusement in the compartment. But I stuck to my guns.

Léonide Savine took me to the step.

'Without my permission,' he said, 'the sentries wouldn't let you go.'

About a kilometre away, I met Marfa. She was exhausted. She had been wandering about the labyrinth of rails for three hours. She had met with nothing but curses when she asked the way to the Cossacks. She could scarcely stand on her legs.

I showed her the way, but added: 'You'd do better to come back with me. In a few hours' time, they'll all be mad drunk.'

'I love him too much,' Marfa replied.

Every succeeding night, I went to The Aquarium. I found there the hysterical Russian, my friend Bob, Harry of the American Marines and Major Robinson, who danced almost naked.

But none of us ever saw Marfa again.

When the authorities of the allied armies succeeded in making Semenoff's train leave Vladivostok, the body of a woman was found under an embankment where the snow had melted more quickly than elsewhere. She had been flayed with a whip.

2

MORE THAN BROTHERS

IT WAS in the early autumn of 1920 that I found myself in London for the first time.

But it was not the red buses circling round Piccadilly, the hieratical changing of the guard at Buckingham Palace, the charm of the great parks, the mysteries of Soho, nor the massive strength, the indestructible grandeur, of the quays and docks that were the object of my study. England and her capital did not interest me at all.

At that time Ireland was struggling savagely and heroically against the British Crown for independence. I was passing through London only in order to acquire the necessary safe conducts for my mission from people who were working secretly for the Irish cause.

I was twenty-two. I was doing my first big journalistic job.

I was excited, dreaming only of Ireland. London, its sights, its underworld and its pleasures did not exist so far as I was concerned.

Only two places in the huge city attracted my passionate attention.

One was the little solicitor's office occupied by Art O'Brien, the Sinn Fein's secret delegate; the other was Brixton Prison.

In Brixton, Terence MacSwiney, Lord Mayor of Cork, was slowly committing suicide by hunger-strike. The eyes of the world were fixed in agonised astonishment on the voluntary dying, the slow renunciation of the flesh, the self-destruction determined by a fierce and fanatical will. He wished it to serve as a symbol of the fate of his country under the yoke and he wanted to be among its martyrs.

Day after day, the Lord Mayor of Cork was letting his life slip away. And, each morning, men all over the world turned to the news which echoed his terrible sacrifice.

When I reached London, Terence MacSwiney had been fasting for sixty-two days. People who saw him in his cell were astonished that so disincarnate a being could still think, feel and talk. They said he looked like a saint. And their accounts were often interrupted by the sobs that rose in their throats.

The day before I left for Ireland, I was saying good-bye to Art O'Brien, when a woman came into his office. She wore a wet, crumpled mackintosh. Her cheap hat had become misshapen under the rain. Her face and expression were unremarkable.

'How is he this evening?' Art O'Brien asked.

Then, turning to me, he said: 'Let me introduce Mrs MacSwiney, Terence's wife.'

In a low level voice, she said: 'Splendid, as always.'

'Do you hope he'll accept food?' I asked, filled with pity for this woman who was watching her husband slip gradually into the shades.

She started, as if I had insulted her.

'You can be assured,' she said in the same level voice, 'that if Terence—though I know God won't permit it—suddenly wished to break his fast, I would prevent his doing so.'

This reply was my introduction to the Irish struggle.

Two days later, I was unpacking my bag in the Shelburne Hotel in Dublin. Though I had not rung for him, the valet came in.

'Mr Desmond wants to see you,' he said.

'Mr Desmond?'

I searched my memory for the name.

'Ask him to wait a moment,' I said.

'You know he can't do that.'

And the valet's lips parted for a moment in a grave, fraternal smile of complicity.

'All right,' I muttered.

'Go in quickly,' the valet whispered to my visitor.

A young man came quickly, silently and furtively into the room. His frank face, the soft glow of his blue eyes and his sharp yet romantic expression all made me take to him at once.

'I'm Desmond Fitzgerald,' he said, 'in charge of Sinn Fein propaganda. Art warned me of your arrival.'

'Art?'

'Art O'Brien.'

'Oh, I'm sorry,' I said, laughing. 'I'm not used to your Christian names yet.'

'I can understand that,' Fitzgerald said, laughing too.

Gaiety suited his youthful, careless, poetical face. He did not look like a conspirator at all. I told him so.

'Oh,' Fitzgerald said, 'when one's condemned to death, one might as well treat it light-heartedly.'

'Condemned to death?'

'It's only the second time.'

'And yet you come to see me in broad daylight in the largest hotel in the town?'

Desmond Fitzgerald laughed louder than ever.

'Don't worry about me,' he said. 'There are quite a number of us walking about Dublin whom the courts-martial have condemned to the gallows. But the whole population is on our side, protects us and hides us. You saw how the floor valet behaved. The whole staff are Sinn Feiners. I'd be warned of danger before the English police reached the hotel. And I've got my bicycle at the servants' door. Look, let's talk seriously. Which of our people do you want to see? Arthur Griffith? Michael Collins? Countess Markiewitz?'

These names were famous then. Irishmen uttered them with fervour; Englishmen with hatred. They meant rebellion to the death, murderous ambushes, pitiless outlawry. Fitzgerald's suggestion was precisely what I had hoped for.

Then we talked of literature. Fitzgerald loved the French symbolists. In the middle of our conversation there was a discreet knock at the door. Fitzerald vanished like a shadow.

A few minutes later I saw him through the window pedalling nonchalantly away.

I saw him nearly every morning, sometimes in the hotel, sometimes in dim alleys or in the back room of an empty flat. He had no lodging. He never slept under the same roof twice. His bicycle seemed to be part of his personality. He told me everything that was going on with the greatest kindness in the world and always ended by quoting poetry.

Thanks to him, I met the leaders of a rebellion which a whole people had been carrying out secretly for centuries, with every now and then a bloody explosion. Thanks to him, I got to know the machinery of a government, of a parliament not recognised by the law and declared traitor by the English. Its leaders had all been condemned to death, and yet it raised taxes, appointed judges and ran an army.

'You've met all our best chaps, I think,' Desmond Fitzgerald said one day. 'All except one, and perhaps the most extraordinary of them all. I'll take you to his house tonight.'

Fitzgerald arranged to meet me on a bridge over the Liffey; and then, as always, vanished rather than went out.

I met him when night fell. We crossed the dark city which was under martial law. Above us was a soft, rainy sky. Fitzgerald was pushing his bicycle.

Every now and then, at a cross-roads, a shadow detached itself from a dark porch and came up to my guide. We then changed our route.

There was an unmistakable charm about this provincial city. Though apparently sleeping, you were aware of a perpetual watch, an incessant condition of alert. We often heard the rhythmic marching of patrols. If we ran into one, Fitzgerald could escape neither prison nor death.

Nevertheless, he talked enthusiastically of Erskine Childers, whom he was taking me to see.

'You can't imagine how much I admire him,' Fitzgerald said. 'He's even more devoted to the cause of Ireland than I am, if that's possible. And yet he's an Englishman. What we have in our blood and what we defend owing to our heredity, he has come to through the heart and from a sense of justice. Isn't that splendid? A fine Englishman, who fought heroically for England in 1914, and has written a magnificent book, and yet he suddenly turns against his own country because he believes its cause to be unjust. Because of that he's more than my brother.'

We had reached a bungalow on the outskirts of Dublin. All around was the peace of a sleeping village; no lights showed from the windows of the house. There was a similar peace in the large, softly lit drawing-room where a man and a woman greeted us.

Mrs Childers was sitting by a wood fire. Her pale, delicate face, her weak but gracious voice, her gentle quivering gestures, all gave her the appearance of a créole slowly dying from some nameless disease. Seldom have I seen a woman in whom such nobility, beauty and patience were united.

Her husband had the face of an intellectual, a prophet. His young eyes gave the lie to his age, which was revealed by silky grey hair and deep lines on his forehead. His face had the irresistible attraction of calm resolution, sensitivity and spiritual grace.

How can one describe the silent understanding, the exquisite tenderness existing between these two people? It was like a living fluid present in the room—a room in which copper shone dully with the reflection of the colours of pictures and rich stuffs.

Time passed imperceptibly in this atmosphere of which, even today, I seem to feel the peculiar charm. Towards midnight, Fitzgerald vanished. I made to go with him.

'Stay another few minutes,' Childers said. 'I want to tell you a splendid story. You know there was a rising in Dublin in 1916, during the war. It failed. It was pitilessly suppressed, as was bound to happen in wartime. It was enough to have been recognised as one of the rebels besieged in the Post Office, the insurrectionists' strongpoint, to be shot. The court-martial tried cases quickly. One witness for the prosecution was enough. Then, when one of the accused, in spite of his protests, was found guilty and condemned to death, a young boy among the public got to his feet: 'I swear,' he said, 'that this man was not in the Post Office.' 'How do you know?' the president of the court asked. 'Because I was there myself,' the boy replied. He was condemning himself to death to save an innocent man. But the members of the court-martial could not bring themselves to sentence him. They sent him merely to life imprisonment. After the war, he was amnestied. And he began the struggle all over again. This time, he was condemned to death in his absence.'

'What was his name?'

'Desmond Fitzgerald,' Childers said.

He looked thoughtfully at the bowl of his pipe. It smelled sweet. He said: 'For that, he's more than my brother.'

Then, when Ireland, despite the whole might of England, extracted the first elements of freedom from the Crown, there were, as always, two parties confronting each other, the moderates and the extremists. The first were content for the moment with the advantages they had obtained. The second considered them insufficient and unacceptable.

A fratricidal war broke out between parties which, till then, had fought in the same sacred cause. Erskine Childers was a supporter of the intransigent De Valera, Fitzgerald supported the cause of the more politic Griffith.

And the government of which Fitzgerald was a member had Childers shot.

'More than my brother,' each of these men had said of the other.

What became of the young woman who sat before the wood fire that autumn night, and to whom I was introduced by an enthusiastic young man living a secret, shelterless life?

3
ILDA

DURING the First World War, Deschamps had been one of my best friends in the squadron. He had stayed on in the army, been posted to Syria, and I had lost sight of him.

One night, when he was on leave, I met him coming out of the Moulin Rouge.

We went to one of Marc-Antoine's nightclubs in Montmartre. Marc-Antoine, once a notorious beggar, had through his courage, intelligence and determination become an important owner of nightclubs. But this did not make him give up his old friends.

I shall never know why, but he had a real, if rather fatherly, affection for me. It was worth extensive credit in all his establishments and at the age I then was this was important to me.

The place to which I took Deschamps was, as usual, full of the most determined seekers of pleasure from the two Americas and, though it was only midnight, the gaiety had already attained to a lively intensity.

Among the wild and merry company, two men stood out for their calmness and sobriety. I recognised Guy and Barbou the Corsican. They were wearing dinner jackets. They signalled an almost imperceptible greeting.

Guy was a man of forty, very thin, hatchet-faced and elegantly dressed. No one in all Montmartre had a more alert mind or a quicker hand. People had often tried to shoot him, but they had always been a second too late.

As for Barbou the Corsican, among other exploits he had travelled to Venezuela for the sole purpose of killing a former accomplice who had betrayed him and got him twelve years' imprisonment.

I quickly gave Deschamps an account of these two men. He had no objection to joining them.

'The reason we're here, dressed up as men about town,' Guy

said, 'is simply for the pleasure of being of use. You see, two drunken Americans started a row here yesterday. Marc-Antoine politely turned them out. They threatened to come back with a gang and break the place up. Marc-Antoine hasn't told us about this, but everything is known in Montmartre. So Barbou and I have come along to keep an eye on things.

An hour went by while we drank champagne and talked peacefully.

Deschamps was getting bored.

'You oughtn't to stay with us,' Guy said. 'The captain's on leave. He needs a woman. Go and have a look in the bar. With his appearance and his rank it won't take long to fix him up.'

We followed his advice. Painted, excited, animated by the music, the hope of gain, alcohol and drugs, a dozen hostesses were chattering in the little room where the barman, whom I had known as an army cook in Vladivostok (one met the whole world in Montmartre), was pouring out potent drinks.

Deschamps' expression became suddenly youthful. He had not changed. There were only two things in the world he cared for: a fast aeroplane and a pretty girl.

Our drinks had not even been served before a woman smiled at Deschamps. She was not a professional. Though she was daringly made-up, her complexion had that brilliant freshness, her skin that fruit-like bloom, which one never sees in the hostesses of nightclubs.

Deschamps offered her a drink. She accepted it without a word, merely with an inclination of the head, and drank it in one gulp. Then she said something quickly in an incomprehensible language. You could tell from her voice that she was very drunk.

Deschamps asked her a question in French. Her only answer was to laugh and show her brilliant teeth. I tried Russian. She stammered a few words in that language, but they were scarcely intelligible and deformed by a very harsh accent. Then she began talking to us in German, but neither Deschamps nor I understood it. Fortunately she also knew English, and so we could more or less carry on a conversation.

At this point, Marc-Antoine came up to wish me good evening and I asked him about his new hostess.

'You're wrong,' he said. 'I don't know her. She's come here for the first time tonight. She's paid for about ten drinks.'

He looked at her attentively and went on: 'But she'll come back and finish like all the others. She's an hysteric.'

'You see drama everywhere,' I replied with a laugh.

Marc-Antoine shook his head and looked at the girl again.

'I wish him luck,' he said.

Meanwhile Deschamps had discovered that the girl's name was Ilda and that she was Finnish.

The smallness of the bar and the crowd were not suitable to the development of a sentimental adventure. Deschamps, as usual, wanted to hurry things along. He suggested going somewhere else. Ilda agreed enthusiastically and demanded a Russian nightclub. We found one in the next street and, as we were all excited, the tziganes, always on the look-out for a party, played their wildest.

Their guitars had voices, their songs fire. Drunkenness, desire, despair, escape and blood in turn imbued their melodies. To the sound of these wild tunes, one drinks without moderation. But, though I was fairly accustomed to these unrestrained orgies, I was appalled by the way Ilda drank. The waiters had scarcely time to fill her glass. She mixed champagne with kummel and vodka. Her eyes grew larger and larger and you could no longer tell whether they shone with joy or despair. One of her shoulder-straps kept slipping down, and if Descamps had not seen to it, she would have been half-naked. She twisted the flowers in her feverish hands.

When my friend kissed her neck or her shoulder she burst out with a haggard, sensual laugh, but if he tried to reach her lips, she ground her teeth in anger, almost in cruelty.

Deschamps soon warmed up at this game and pressed Ilda to go home with him. At first, she did not appear to understand, then began neighing (I can find no other word to describe her laugh), drank off two full glasses of her appalling mixture and got to her feet. But before she reached the door, her head swam. Deschamps had to use both his strong arms to hold her upright.

'See you tomorrow,' he called to me.

A guitarist came and sat beside me, a singer opposite, and I forgot everything else in the world. I do not know how much later it was when the door of the nightclub burst open with a clatter and I heard Deschamps' voice saying, 'Pay quickly and come. I'll be waiting outside in a taxi.'

His voice was so urgent, his face so pale, and his whole appearance so strange for a man of his stamp, that I sobered up at once. Moreover, his right hand was bound up in a handkerchief and blood was showing through it.

I joined him, jumping into the taxi whose door was waiting open.

'Where are we going?' I asked.

'Just drive around,' Deschamps shouted to the taxi-driver.

It was only then I saw a dim, still figure lying on the seat. I murmured, 'It's . . .'

'Yes, it's Ilda,' Deschamps interrupted nervously. 'You can talk out loud, she can't hear.'

'But I've got nothing to say. It's up to you.'

'Yes, of course . . .'

And as the taxi drove past the crude lights of the pleasure haunts, my friend told me the following story:

'I saw that Ilda was drunk all right, but on the whole I was rather pleased, thinking things would go quickly and that we'd have a good sleep afterwards. I made serious advances to her in the taxi till we reached the Avenue Victor-Hugo, where she told me she had a furnished flat. She let me have my way and laughed all the time like a madwoman. The Place de Termes . . . the Étoile . . . we were three minutes from her flat. At that moment, as I was clasping her a little closer, she took my hand and bit me in the palm hard enough to remove the flesh. In fact, I think she did take a bit out, for she immediately spat out my blood. Wolf's teeth. I don't know what I would have done if the taxi hadn't stopped at that moment. She led me indoors without a word. She was trembling, shivering, distraught. I followed her. My hand left a dark trail on the stair-carpet. Three storeys up she took a key from her bag and, though dead-drunk, set about opening the door with a care and a noiselessness that gave me cold shivers down the spine. At last, she pushed it open and, forgetting my presence, tiptoed into the dining-room. On the table was a little box. At first, I thought I was seeing things. And then . . . and then I realised what it was: a little coffin with a tiny dead child in it. Ilda turned and I sensed she was going to laugh again. I lost control. I put my bloody hand over her mouth. I dragged her outside and slammed the door—oh, the noise, the noise!—and brought her back to where I had left you. She fell asleep at once. She's passed out . . .'

We carried Ilda into a hotel which was kept by a friend of Guy's.

'Let her sleep it off,' Deschamps said to him. 'She'll wake up soon enough.'

I have often seen Ilda since then. She became a hostess at Marc-Antoine's.

4
THE MAN WHO LIKED HOLOCAUSTS

ON THAT January evening in 1930 there was a big dinner at the Imperial Palace in Addis Ababa.

The Ethiopian sovereign was the same then as now. But he did not yet call himself Haile Selassie. He went by the title of Negus Taffari. But that made no difference to the pomp of the ceremony.

It was a pomp which—like everything else in that strange town—was a mixture of the Abyssinian protocol of the Middle Ages and the most modern European customs. Sitting at the Negus' table were old warriors with ebony faces, dressed in the traditional white *chamma*, of which the huge billowing folds reminded one of the classical toga, and diplomats in tail-coats. Slaves with animal-like faces, who to the last drop of their and their descendants' blood were their master's property, waited on the guests, while on the dining-room wall, in a place of honour, was an aeroplane propeller in the hub of which French mechanics had ingeniously fitted a clock.

The food and drink contrasted in the same way. Dishes suited to a Parisian palate were served side by side with *inghira*, a sort of heavy paste which took the place of bread, spread with *watt*, a disgusting sauce of red barberry. Bottles of champagne stood next to jugs of *tetch*, a heady, intoxicating hydromel, the favourite drink of the Abyssinian nobility.

The Negus was wearing a black cloak. Across his chilly knees was a lion-skin. On each side of him was a lady in an elegant low-cut evening dress.

Opposite the sovereign sat a child with dark eyes and curly hair. This was the Crown Prince. On his right was the British consul; on his left, the Italian tank-instructor.

Nor did the mixture end there. By their uniforms, I recognised the Belgian officer in charge of drill and the Swedish officer in charge of the artillery. Finally, at the other end of the table, my friend Maillet smiled at me with his frank and manly smile, showing his white teeth. He had been a French pilot during the Great War, had escaped from a German prison camp, had pioneered flying in Indo-China and was now commander of the Ethiopian air force.

In short, I knew the names and appointments of all the guests. All, that is, except those of the man sitting immediately opposite me. I would probably not have noticed him if his unusual attire for a ceremonial dinner had not immediately attracted my attention.

He was wearing a blue jacket and white flannel trousers.

When greeting the Negus, he had explained his clothes, in the broadest of American accents, by saying: 'I guess I've just come from tennis and I've had no time to change, boss."

He had accompanied his words with a sort of cordial neigh, and had then proceeded to drink down half a dozen cocktails one after the other.

He was a very tall man with wide shoulders. His face bore an expression of hard and intense greed; he had carnivorous teeth, a narrow forehead and high cheekbones, which were always in movement, like billiard balls.

He drank an incredible amount and talked in a loud voice without caring if anyone were listening.

When dinner was over, I asked Maillet who the man was. Maillet had been at the Negus' court for a long time and knew a great deal.

'I don't know,' my friend said. 'I know nothing about that American, except that his name is Jack Jackson. He arrived yesterday. But why he's here, what he does and who introduced him are mysteries.'

A week went by, and it seemed to go as quickly as a short day. I lived in a sort of perpetual enchantment. Addis Ababa was unlike any other town in the world; it lay at an altitude of ten thousand feet, amid great eucalyptus-trees. It acted on me like a spell.

The air was fresh. The sun generous. The streets swarmed with a crowd you could never tire of watching. Warriors armed with curved swords and lances, half-naked Gallas, Chankella slaves scarcely removed from primitive animality, Somalis proud as classical bronzes, Issa and Danakil caravaneers, indeed all the black tribes from Upper Egypt to the Red Sea mingled in the streets and squares.

Greek, Armenian and Maltese merchants displayed their wares in the open air.

The *toucouls*—conical huts—built with no sort of alignment, added to the chaos created by the population.

The luxury cars from the legations moved slowly through the crowd, which made reluctant way for them. But the noisy crowd had only to hear the warning shouts of the runner preceding some high Abyssinian nobleman and his escort to scatter as if by enchantment. Then an impassive, haughty, bearded warrior would amble past on a mule with red leather saddlery. Behind him came his soldiers and slaves. Beside him ran a slave with a fly-whisk.

These thousand sights, which changed with every hour of the day, fused into one huge and splendid fresco on the feast of St Michael when, each year, the high Coptic clergy proceeded to the blessing of the altar stones removed from the churches of Addis Ababa for the occasion.

Only a film taken by a cameraman of genius could have expressed the towering magnificence, the grandiose beauty of a spectacle in which the rites of the desert, the charms of nature, the age-old ceremonies of a curious cult, the concourse of an immense crowd, and the presence of the last black emperor, with his court, were fused in seemingly endless rejoicing.

There were frenzied dances in the squares, performed by whole tribes gathered in perpetually moving circles, while witch-doctors whipped the bare legs of the performers to make them jump higher; there was endless, ecstatic chanting, hysterical wailing, shouting and howling as the black crowds gave way to a pagan excitement, an exaltation of dervishism born of the jungle and the desert.

And all this was only the prelude to the real ceremony, which took place outside the town in a vast clearing surrounded by gently sloping hills covered with giant eucalyptus.

Every hill carried spectators; there were at least a hundred thousand men present. One hundred thousand ebony bodies, clothed in one hundred thousand white tunics, in tiers beneath the pale green foliage of the eucalyptus-trees—such was the background.

In the centre of this fantastic amphitheatre, the priests danced to the sound of drums, flutes and cymbals. They wore purple, coral and emerald silk robes. Long flexible canes quivered in their hands as if the shrill, monotonous rhythm had cast a spell on them. They advanced, backed and whirled as they sang. And others, bearing the heavy altar stones on their heads, stood motionless as idols, watching the ageless choreography which made you think of the dance before the Ark.

Madmen rolled screaming on the ground. At one end of the clearing the Negus, surrounded by his officers, ministers and most powerful chiefs, sat on a golden throne. How slender and puny he looked, how chilly in spite of his lion-skin, amid the tough figures of his favourite *ras*!

Only one white face stood out against the background of dark ones. And, to my profound astonishment, I recognised in the distance the blue coat and flannel trousers which had so much surprised me at the Negus' dinner. It was Jack Jackson.

His eyes were closed and he was chewing gum.

Addis Ababa was really the most extraordinary town. It even had a nightclub in its neighbourhood. It was called Robinson, and it was run by a Greek.

It was situated some twelve kilometres from the capital, at the point where the carriage-road ended. I was taken there by some friends on the evening of the feast of St Michael. Of all the contrasts which tested my nerves in Addis Ababa, one of the most violent was undoubtedly to pass suddenly from a mystical and barbarian celebration to a sort of mediocre provincial nightclub.

The walls were hung with pink, flowered hangings. Four musicians scraped out waltzes, fox-trots and tangos. The little lamps on the tables were covered with shades in almost pathetic bad taste. The ash-trays bore the names of important French firms.

And this is why I remember the ash-trays so well . . .

The Greek proprietor said sadly: 'It's not possible to drink, sir.'

'Why?' one of us asked.

'I've got no more glasses or cups,' he groaned.

He lowered his voice, pointed to the corner of the room and murmured: 'The gentleman over there has broken everything. He has paid and paid well. I can't complain about that. But I was very frightened. And the whole room emptied.'

Perhaps our voices woke the sleeper up. I do not know. But anyway he sat up; and the coarse face and wide shoulders of Jack Jackson appeared above the table-cloth.

'Hullo!' he said jovially. 'I'll buy you a drink.'

'In what?' the Greek sighed.

'In the ash-trays,' Jackson said as if it were the most natural thing in the world. 'Have them washed in my presence!'

The man was obviously very drunk, but with that lucid, semi-visionary drunkenness which is sometimes the permanent state of alcoholics.

Jack Jackson took off his coat. Under his silk shirt you could see the play of powerful, splendid muscles, the muscles of a great cat. He had the look of a boxer, a body conditioned to every form of excess, and a disturbingly cruel expression. He was in splendid form.

We drank to each other out of the ash-trays.

Jackson came and sat beside me.

'What are you selling?' he asked abruptly.

'Nothing,' I said.

'How right you are, especially in this goddamned country!' he cried. 'I've brought their damned nigger of a king the best deal in the world. Do you know whom I'm representing?'

He searched his pockets and brought out, together with bundles of dollars, half-a-dozen business cards. They bore the names of the greatest United States' armament firms.

'That's why you were received better than an ambassador!' I said.

Jackson looked at me in stupefaction and laughed.

'Do you expect that damned nigger to keep an American waiting?'

Then, growing excited, he went on: 'I'm always welcome everywhere,' he said proudly. 'I know how to choose the countries where they need me. I've sold aircraft and machine-guns to Chinese marshals, mountain-guns to Albania, rifles to Ireland, grenades to the Hedjaz. I smell war and revolution from a distance. I've a flair for it, and I've got credit.'

He poured brandy into his ash-tray, emptied it and went on: 'I'll bet a bag of dollars to a bag of powder that blood will be flowing here soon. So I came. I've offered the little black king aircraft, munitions, and the latest model machine-guns—wonderful stuff, jewels. And instructors as well. I sell instructors too. Last year, I supplied forty to Guatemala.'

'What happened?' I asked.

'Well, he said yes and no, and then yes and no again. I was so bloody angry I came away and got real drunk.'

He reflected for a moment or two, put his powerful hand on my arm and said: 'You saw that carnival of theirs this morning? Don't you think they'd have done better to give me a few orders?'

'And where are you going next?' one of my friends asked.

'This year, to Cuba. Later, to Spain.'

The merchant in death had a nose for holocausts.

5
THE KILLER WITH WHITE TEETH

I WAS finishing dinner alone in a restaurant near the Champs-Elysées, absent-mindedly watching the coming and going of customers, the behaviour of couples, the play of faces and eyes between tables, the automatic smiles and grimaces of the waiters. The Parisian comedy found in a fashionable restaurant held little amusement for me. I impatiently ordered coffee.

'Filter? Turkish? Cona?' the waiter inquired.

'I don't mind,' I said, 'but bring it quickly.'

'Turkish then, sir,' the waiter said. 'We've got a new Indian who makes it perfectly.'

Soon the waiter's 'Indian' came to my table, preceded by a brass tray. He was dressed in tawdry, gold-embroidered clothes, no doubt hired from a theatrical costumier. On his head was an enormous fez.

His clothes and his caricature of the ritual greeting, putting his right hand to his heart, mouth and forehead, were grotesque.

But there was more to come.

When the black waiter had straightened up and his eyes met mine, he suddenly began trembling, shivering as if from an attack of malaria. Hot coffee poured from the pot and burnt my knees.

I made to get up, but was prevented. Supernaturally strong arms were clasped about me and a bare, woolly head was pressed against my chest. Through a mixture of sobs and childish laughter, I heard: 'My master . . . my master . . . Daouenlé! Issa! Danakil!'

It was not so much these guttural stammerings which suddenly aroused in my memory's eye a whole fresco of wonderful and extraordinary pictures, but rather the smell of the dark, woolly hair and above all the contact, through the vile clothes, of those preternaturally strong, tense muscles.

'Moussa!' I cried.

But I still could not believe it. I had to seize the face hidden in my coat and raise it to mine. I had to gaze at the delighted features, see the teeth shine, count the scars on the cheeks, really to discover, in that face which a few moments before had been dishonoured by the fez and the servile bowing and scraping, the nobility of the savage, the purity of the desert and the recollection of great adventure.

'Moussa!' I murmured, recovering my breath. 'Moussa . . .'

I might have embraced him had not the waiter, looking anxious and disapproving, approached at that moment.

I became aware of the attention I was attracting, the sniggering of women, jokes being bandied. I blushed. Not for the diners, nor for myself. Not even for Moussa. But for my memories.

How could I explain them? How could I defend them to these puppets who were wound up again each night?

I paid, told Moussa where to meet me, and went off towards the quays to give my memories an airing beside the dark Seine.

It was in Abyssinia, at the time when the Emperor Haile Selassie still called himself Ras Taffari.

I had had no time to linger over the delights of Addis Ababa, the capital, where, at an altitude of ten thousand feet, the sovereign led his singular life in his *guebi*,[1] and there were nobles dressed in lion-skins, Greek and Armenian merchants, beggars, slaves and prostitutes displaying their black faces and shaven heads in *toucouls*[2] decorated with a red cross.

My assignment was to study the slave trade on both shores of the Red Sea. Three friends accompanied me in my search for the traces of the slave-traders. And we had a key man to help us do it: Henri de Monfreid.

Today, Monfreid is famous. Everyone knows at least some episodes of his adventurous and legendary life. But at that period he was quite unknown in France. Between his mysterious journeys, he grew coffee in the Haramé oasis to which a little road from Harar, an Arab walled town, ran between patches of euphorbia.

While interrogating slaves in the province of Harar and shooting in the deep, virgin valleys, we had concerted a plan for a dangerous expedition. We had decided to follow the route by which the caravans took their human freight from Abyssinia to the creeks on the

[1] Palace. [2] Straw huts.

African coast of the Red Sea where the Yemenite dhows loaded it for the Asian shore.

Our route left Ethiopian territory at the railway linking Jibuti to the Abyssinian capital, crossed French Somaliland through desert and almost uncontrolled districts to Lake Assal, and on to the Gulf of Tajura, where Monfreid was to be waiting for us with his boat.

We arrived at Daouenlé on a fine evening. It was the last Ethiopian station on the Franco-Abyssinian railway. At Dire Dawa, which was then the biggest European centre in Abyssinia, we had collected our saddle and pack-mules, our equipment, two Somali boys, a Galla muleteer and Djamma, half Abyssinian and half Danakil, who had been a sergeant of colonial troops.

Daouenlé, like other stations on the line, consisted of a dozen huts, built near the water-tank at which the panting little locomotives drank. These huts reflected a mean and hopeless poverty, wretched as their cracked walls and the dirty straw that roofed them.

The station itself was only a miserable shed. A few natives were working in it. The sun and undernourishment had reduced their bare, emaciated limbs to skeletons. An old man was directing them in a dull, hoarse voice.

His features were hidden by a white beard and his face was completely expressionless. He was a Greek and had emigrated from the mountains of Thessaly at the end of the last century. He had worked on the railway, which he never left, for thirty years. Most of the time he spoke only the local dialects, but he still knew a few words of French. He had no curiosity. The arrival of three Europeans did not in the least excite him. These phantoms from another world awakened no gleam in his tired eyes.

What did they matter to him? Even when he had leave, he never went to Jibuti or even nearby Dire Dawa. Daouenlé, with its sordid huts and its half-starved population, was his whole universe.

The rocky desert, without tree or shadow, began a few paces from the station. But the old Greek, in his torn and dirty white clothes, did not see it. His eyes were always staring at the ground.

He was the very image of dull and melancholy solitude. With his stooping shoulders and the thick, knotted bones revealed by his emaciation, he was like an old dead tree.

'You'll have to spend the night with me,' he said.

We knew it. The leader of our caravan, the *abane*, the guide and guarantor of our safety, was not due to arrive from his tribe till dawn next day. The Greek's expressionless voice made us regret a camp under the desert stars more than ever.

The brief twilight had long gone by the time our men had finished unloading the mules. The young moon lit up the tops of the huts and the rocks which rose to the north like flotsam on a formless sea. In the morning, our caravan would set out through them.

As we looked at this barrier which stood between us and adventure, after a few seconds our eyes became accustomed to the dusk and we saw a white figure standing at the foot of a needle of rock. We took a few paces towards it. It came forward as if to meet us, but passed us and continued on its way towards the tottering station building. The old Greek seemed to have failed to recognise us.

'A funny chap!' one of us muttered. 'What a gay dinner we'll have tonight!'

Yet, when we went into his living-room, furnished with a truckle-bed, a rough table and a few empty packing-cases, it became clear that the solitary of Daouenlé had done his best to welcome his unexpected guests. There were plates of native pottery at everyone's place. And an omelette was cooking on a paraffin stove. The old man slowly opened tins with his big, trembling, heavily veined hands.

We protested. Had we not abundant supplies, boys, a cook?

'No, no,' the Greek muttered, without raising his eyes. 'Not at all. You're my guests. It wouldn't be right.'

His blundering, expressionless voice betrayed an innate and obstinate determination to be hospitable. Perhaps it was an unconscious need to thank such travellers as conferred the boon of their presence on him. We dared not refuse, and merely had a few bottles of our best wine brought from our baggage.

The meal took place in silence. The old man chewed with difficulty and made no attempt to talk. He just sipped once at the glass of wine our boy had placed beside him.

'Just to welcome you,' he said, raising his pale, dull eyes to us for a second. 'I no longer know how to drink.'

Taking advantage of the opening, I did my best to start a

conversation. I asked our host whether he intended returning to Europe.

'What for?' he replied.

Then, with the effort and difficulty of a man who has not expressed his thoughts aloud for a long time past, he added: 'I've got no one. My daughter died here. I buried her.'

He made a vague gesture towards the rocks where we had seen him in the moonlight a little while ago.

'She was a little girl,' he went on. 'She was outside. Some Issas came to attack the Danakils. She was in their path. It's thirty years ago now. It's quiet here these days, very quiet. The trains don't run at night.'

We put up our camp beds. The old man on his truckle-bed went to sleep first. He talked a lot in his sleep, in a strange language in which Abyssinian and Somali were mingled with Greek.

I had never practised the profession of caravan-leader. Nor had my friends. One was an army doctor, the other a naval officer. We were counting on our native servants. We were wrong.

Djamma had courage and spoke French very well but, as a foreman in a horse-hair factory, he knew nothing of mules or pack-saddles. The two Somali boys knew how to polish shoes and prepare a simple meal, but that was all. As for Haile, the muleteer, he seemed completely half-witted.

For an hour we impotently watched our cases falling about and the kicking of maddened mules. The few dozen inhabitants of the village watched our difficulties impassively. Only the naked, rachitic children laughed a good deal.

However, things suddenly took another turn.

The old Greek, who had disappeared some moments before in the direction of the huts, made his way back towards us through the group of spectators on the railway embankment. He was followed by a man who, though very black of skin, seemed made of a different material from the weak and sickly villagers. He was physically splendid, from his neck, planted like a column on his bronze shoulders, to his slender, proud legs. He was naked except for an exiguous loin-cloth about his narrow hips. From it hung a dagger in a raw-hide sheath.

'Moussa, the butcher,' the old Greek said.

Moussa set to work at once. In his hands, the whole business seemed merely a game. The heavy cases appeared to weigh no more than corks in his arms. They stacked themselves on their own. The most restive mules obeyed his irresistible will. He laughed all the time and his strong, magnificently white teeth shone out from his broad, black, rather snub-nosed face, with its fine, ram-like forehead. I watched him work with delight. A vigorous man's body at work is always a fine sight. But when that vigour is clothed in faultless muscle, rippling with power and supple precision, beneath a sort of dark silk gleaming in the sun, one seems to be watching some perfect barbaric statue come alive.

Such was Moussa.

'Surely he's not of the same race as those other wretched people?' I asked the old Greek.

'Yes,' the Greek said. 'He's an Issa too.'

He paused for a few seconds, as if searching for forgotten words before going on.

'But he comes from a tribe from out there.'

He pointed to the desert.

At this point, the *abane* arrived.

He was a tall Issa, and so thin that his black skin seemed to be merely a sheath for his bones. But his quick, precise movements, his shining eyes, his forehead and long hair smeared with rancid butter, and the folds of his tattered robes, all gave a feeling of space, movement and savage freedom. You saw at once that he, too, was a man of the desert.

He was carrying a tall stick that reached as high as the curls of his hair. At his belt he wore a dagger across his hollow stomach.

The old Greek guaranteed his loyalty, but nevertheless advised us to leave the salary agreed on for the *abane's* services at Daouenlé. It would be given him when he returned with a note from us.

To this the guide agreed. On another point, however, he proved intractable.

'I shall go no farther than Dikkil,' the *abane* said three times. 'Whatever you offer me, I shall take the foreigners no farther. And I must have a promise before witnesses that I shall not be asked to do so.'

The whole population of the village had come to watch our departure. They supported the *abane* with shrill cries.

We asked his reasons. But the old man remained as dumb and indifferent as if he had not heard.

'He's proud,' Djamma said, 'He's the chief of a tribe. He doesn't want to admit that the territory beyond Dikkil is forbidden his people because it belongs to the Danakils. He might get through all right with you, because you are white and have rifles which can shoot many bullets one after the other. But he'd certainly have his throat cut on the way back.'

Djamma spoke with unconscious pride. Through his mother, he was half Dankali. And the strength of this blood-tie was such that even though he had spent six years in France and now, in Abyssinia, was headman of a French expedition, he could still share the hatred and contempt of his maternal ancestors for the age-old enemy.

For the origin of the unquenchable, inexpiable quarrel between Danakils and Issas was lost in the mists of time. And this, more than anything else, gave the measure of the tenacity with which its roots were sunk in their inflexible hearts.

Why did Moussa join us? It had occurred to no one to engage him. Was it because of the pay, which seemed to him fabulous? Was it because the loading had amused him? Or was he simply unable to resist the appeal of a caravan setting out amid a noise of hooves, shouts and weapons? I am inclined to think the last explanation the correct one.

However, without a word to anyone, and merely his dagger and a little prayer carpet of ill-tanned leather thrown over his left shoulder for baggage, Moussa suddenly appeared beside me as we were passing through the short defile which led to the Issa desert. The brilliant bar of his teeth illumined his face. He took his place beside the *abane* at the head of the caravan.

During the course of my travels, I had known other inhuman regions. I had crossed the Syrian desert, and approached the Rio de Oro. I had gone down into the stifling basin in which lie the thick and sticky waters of the Dead Sea. But none of these desolate places could rival the intensity of the harshness, the banefulness of the horror of the territory behind the barrier of rocks that covered Daouenlé on the north.

Apart from the sky, in which the sun rose like a devouring monster, intolerably bright to unacclimatised eyes, everything was black. As far as the eye could see, the landscape presented nothing but a succession of black mountains and black hollows. There was not a shrub, not a blade of grass. The sole vegetation consisted of black stones, black rocks and black gravel. It was a rocky, rugged, broken, dull black land, its hills strewn with dark avalanches, depressions like mourning strands and funeral stones which clattered beneath the mules' hooves and the men's feet. The whole world seemed to have been burnt up in a Cyclopean fire and covered with a layer of petrified soot.

In this infernal arena, even the rays of the sun seemed lifeless. Their fascicle weighed down almost like some solid element and remained captive, immobile, without change or vibration, caught in the mass of the black rocks, stones and dust and became one with them in a strange carboniferous blaze.

The *abane*, hard as the stick he carried, his naked buttocks hollowing slightly at each step beneath the white cotton garment that covered the upper part of his body, seemed to be part of the landscape. He knew every outline of this sombre land. He had its strength and its cruel asceticism. He led our caravan till nightfall at a steady, untiring pace, without saying a word or touching the goatskin water-bag he carried at his waist beside his dagger, and which contained, within its damp, stinking envelope, the source of life that every desert dweller instinctively economises.

He did not stop till the setting sun began to turn the dark land red with an apocalyptic fire. He then placed on the ground an untanned hide he carried on his shoulder, knelt on its rough surface and prostrated himself. It was the evening prayer.

At this moment, we saw a strange outline crowning a hillock and standing out against the black and purple horizon. It formed a rough quadrilateral, evidently built by human hands. As we drew nearer, we descried fairly high walls made of heavy stones roughly heaped on each other. On their summits others had been erected that seemed as sharp as sword-blades or arrows. Fragments of cloth hung from them.

'There was a big battle here,' Djamma said. 'Danakil warriors came to water here on Issa land. The well is not far away. They killed many herdsmen belonging to the enemy tribe. This is their tomb. And every one of them their brothers buried here had been deprived, you may be sure, of what makes a man.'

The caravan passed silently by the barbaric tomb beneath which the vanquished and mutilated warriors slept safe from jackals and hyenas.

'Did it happen long ago?' I asked Djamma, who was walking beside my mule.

'Half a dozen years ago, sir,' the former sergeant replied, 'not more.'

Yet we were travelling through French territory which, in theory, was subdued.

A little farther on we came to a well, and here we halted.

Throughout this exhausting day, Moussa had kept an eye on everything. He ran from one end of the caravan to the other, tightening girths, readjusting loads, and urging on laggard mules.

He continued indefatigable at the halt. He lit the fires, and built a thorn fence to protect the mules. One of them escaped into the night. It was Moussa who caught it, saving it from the hyenas whose howling could be heard beyond the camp fires. In short, he was the caravan's black angel with the brilliant smile.

We reached Dikkil next day.

Consisting of an agglomeration of huts and hovels and a few pitiful fields of *dourah* bounded by the sterile land, it was in fact a poor and melancholy oasis of small and dusty palm-trees. But a night at Daouenlé and forty-eight hours among the black rocks had sufficed to change the way we looked at things.

Dikkil seemed to us a privileged place. At its boundary the sombre spell of the desert ceased. The pale leaves of the palms assumed a wonderful intensity. The lamentable crops had something miraculous about them. And how can one express the comfort of finding white men whose every word one understood amid a wild, dark-skinned people who spoke an unknown tongue?

At Dikkil, there were two officers in charge of the district. One was short and fat, had a little black moustache and spoke Parisian slang; the other was a very young and very thin Corsican with an emaciated face and a small red beard.

They met us at the bottom of the steep slope that led up to Dikkil fort. The younger cried, 'You've provided us with one of the greatest excitements of our lives here. Just take a look . . .'

We were entering the courtyard of the outpost.

Somali soldiers were still standing to the loopholes, rifles at the ready. Two machine-guns were pointing in the direction from which we had come. From the neighbouring slopes, the whole population of the oasis, their woolly black heads peeping over hedges and walls, was watching us with a mixture of curiosity and panic.

'What a deployment of forces!' one of us joked. 'Were you expecting an attack?'

'It's because of you,' the administrator laughed. 'One of our Issas reported your caravan an hour ago. He didn't see the Europeans among the men and mules. And no caravan as large as yours, and equipped as yours is, has ever come to Dikkil by the desert of black stones. Our patrolman saw your guns glittering. He took the cases on the mules for machine-guns. We immediately thought that Danakils, led by renegade Abyssinians, were on their way to sack the oasis.'

They both laughed once again. But when we looked at them in astonishment that they could actually have believed such a thing, they became serious and the elder went on: 'You needn't think we're crazy. In this country you can expect anything from travellers passing through it. You've seen the desert between Daouenlé and here. The land is as empty in every direction. For miles and miles around, any band of men you meet is either hungry or on the warpath. They travel quickly and they kill quickly. They can cover a hundred kilometres a day by defiles and short cuts no one else knows. We have *dourah* flour, camels and goats here. It's a great temptation.'

'Particularly since the marauders, whoever they may be, will always find support from half the village,' the young Corsican said. 'The fact is that Dikkil is on the frontier between the Issas and the Danakils. Before we came here, the tribes were regularly cutting each other's throats for possession of the water, the palm-trees and the soil. The recent setting-up of an outpost here has imposed a truce on them. The village is divided into two quite distinct parts and, if we relaxed our hold for a moment, they'd be at each other's throats at the drop of a hat.'

We were treated with splendid hospitality. The two men placed all their meagre resources at our disposal. They emptied their ill-stocked cellar. In their every gesture, in every expression of their bronzed faces, there was a real warmth of friendliness and welcome. They insisted we should have the coolest rooms. Our mules' harness, the saddles and pack-saddles, all our caravan's gear, was examined and repaired. They selected the best guides for us.

When all was ready, the outpost commander said: 'Watch out, for from here to Lake Assal and on to Gubbet Kharab on the Gulf of Tajura—and that's a good week's march—we have no control whatever. The Danakil tribes are to all intents and purposes unsubdued. Others come down from the Awash which, though theoretically belonging to Ethiopia, is in fact a free state of plunderers. The defiles are suited to ambushes. The guides I've selected for you come from those districts. They're the most loyal I have, but I can't guarantee them because I have no hostages. You've got supplies and splendid weapons. They're a temptation. You've been warned.'

But we were a group of seven well-armed men. With that instinct for defiance known to every adventurous traveller, I happily gave the signal for departure.

At that moment there was a disturbance in the ordered line of our caravan. Moussa placed his powerful hand on the withers of my mule and, his athletic shoulders bowed in sign of supplication, began talking volubly.

'What's he saying?' I asked Djamma, the ex-Somali sergeant who commanded our little native escort.

'He says, sir,' Djamma translated slowly, 'that you have been good to him, that you're going into dangerous country and that he beseeches you to take him with you to protect you.'

I hesitated. I liked Moussa's strength, his good humour on the march and at work, his laugh and the way he looked at you. But I was aware of a sort of incredulity in Djamma's voice. I glanced at him questioningly.

'It's impossible, sir,' he said. 'You can't take an Issa into the Danakils' territory.'

He lowered his voice and added: 'I know their tribe well. It was my mother's.'

'And who in this empty desert is to know we've got an Issa with us?'

'The guides,' Djamma replied, still speaking low.

'The guides are in our employment,' I said. 'What we do is none of their business. If Moussa wants to come with us, he may. And so that everyone shall know that I'll answer for his life as for my own, he'll march near me and sleep beside me.'

'As you wish, sir, if it is the will of Allah,' Djamma murmured.

Moussa kissed my hands and rubbed his woolly head against my chest.

We had three guides.

Undoubtedly the most picturesque of them was called Sultan Mohammed. I have never known precisely over whom or what he reigned. But he had a right to a mule, a double ration of rice, sugar and dates, double pay and an umbrella. His companions showed a lively respect for him. He was quite young, had a delicate face, brown rather than black, and wore a tunic of blue silk above a long nether garment of soft, rich colours.

Of the two Danakils who attended him, one had a remarkable appearance. Though the simile of a bird of prey may be a banal description of certain faces, in this instance there is no other to describe that thin face, those cruel, close-set, bloodshot little eyes, and that hard, thin-lipped mouth. His body gave the same impression as his face. It was thin, violent and as dangerous as a hair-trigger. Amid the sinister quiet with which all the men walked, his footsteps had a quality of peculiar silence which aroused that instinctive sense of danger every man feels among virgin lands and their inhabitants.

'He is the greatest warrior in Sultan Mohammed's clan. He is his bodyguard,' Djamma told me at the first midday halt.

We were surrounded by an infernal chaos of black rocks in whose hollow, by some miracle, there was a stagnant pool of sulphurous water at which men and beasts must drink.

'Yes, a great warrior,' Djamma went on with a curious mixture of pride and respect. 'It is certainly true that he has killed at least eight men.'

'How do you know?' I asked.

Djamma stared at me in amazement.

'Count the bracelets on his left arm,' he said.

I saw eight thin strips of dried skin round the man's biceps.

'The relics of the virility of the men he has killed,' Djamma went on. 'And you can be sure the elders of the tribe have confirmed it.'

Moussa interrupted us to hand me, with his delightful smile, the gourd he had filled with water for me. And I counted three bracelets of brown skin round the muscles of his left arm.

'Moussa too?' I asked.

'Of course, sir,' Djamma replied calmly. 'Moussa has deprived three Danakils of their virility.'

Nevertheless, with a gesture of infinite gentleness, Moussa was inclining the neck of the gourd towards my mouth as if giving a drink to a child.

Funereal gorges, haunted by noisy demons; ink-dark plains of lava; small tufts of palms of which the milk inebriates; hot springs; hills of black stones on which the mules stumbled as the caravan moved like a long boat over a sea of dark, still waves; camp fires in the overwhelming solitude; the low noises made by men and animals in the dusk; the undefined danger prowling round the camp; sleep, with the night sky for shelter and one's rifle within reach; the stony desert, even more desert than those of sand; the heat of the sun; the healthy exhaustion of the body returned to nature; the anxiety and joy of finding the water-point . . .

Throughout these fatigues and dangers, Moussa, the black athlete, was my bodyguard and my nurse. It was he who lit my fire and cooked my rice. Since, like the others, I had neither mattress nor pillow, it was Moussa who with his strong arm removed the stones from the accursed ground to make me a softer bed and always succeeded in finding enough wan grasses on which to lay my head. And, often, when awakened by the sting of an insect or the cry of an animal, I would find him crouching beside me, his savage ear on the alert, his night-sighted eyes searching the dark.

Towards the end of these exhausting days during which we covered as much as twenty-five miles of trackless ground under a fiery sky, he would have carried me had I allowed it. And he was always laughing like a tutelary spirit.

It was in the Gongouta defile that our relations with the Danakils took an ugly turn.

The trouble had in fact been brewing for some time. Our guides protested that the caravan was going too fast and that they were overworked. Sultan Mohammed did not get off his mule even when

I and my friends did, which was every alternate hour, to give the animals a rest. This I was compelled to tolerate. A kinglet has a right to his prerogatives.

But I was not prepared to allow that his two companions, warriors capable of covering enormous distances at high speed, should do less than ill-trained Europeans. Djamma gave me the reason for their attitude. I had made a mistake, he said, in coming to terms with the Sultan by the day instead of for the whole job. Gorged on sugar, rice and dates, paid according to the duration of the journey, he and his followers had only one concern, which was to prolong the journey as much as possible. Since I would not listen to them, they began to show their teeth. The warrior with the eight trophies, in particular, became more obstinate and insolent with each stage.

The stage which had brought us to the outskirts of the Gongouta gorges had certainly been the worst of the whole journey. We had had to cross the Gangadi plain, a sort of huge lake of fine sand with sharp ridges, a basin in which the heat was almost murderous. We had not even stopped at dusk, but had marched late into the night by the light of hurricane-lamps to reach the water-point. On the other hand, we were now only a day's march from Lake Assal. There, we were to part from our guides and descend to the Gulf of Gubbet Kharab where Monfreid was awaiting us with his boat.

We had defeated the latent resistance of Sultan Mohammed and his companions. But the mules were very exhausted. They needed to be watered and fed as soon as possible and allowed some rest before the next day's stage.

I issued orders through Djamma that everyone must set to work at once; everyone except, of course, Sultan Mohammed. But his bodyguard lay down beside him with studied nonchalance and refused to move.

The appalling heat and fatigue of the day had had their effect on my nerves. I shook the Dankali and indicated the water-point. He slowly sat up and said, 'I'm a warrior'—Djamma translated—'and not your servant like Moussa of the flat face.'

I may have been wrong to order a warrior to perform a duty which was unacceptable to his pride, but since I had ordered it I had to see that I was obeyed. Otherwise I would have immediately lost face with everyone.

'You'll go at once!' I shouted at him.

Of course, I did not understand the precise meaning of his reply, but I knew that it was an insult. I thoughtlessly raised my hand to him.

If you tread on a snake, he is no quicker to defend himself than a Dankali. He leapt to his feet and, in the same instant movement, drew his dagger. But there was another blade shining in the firelight. Moussa had placed himself between us. I drew my revolver and said: 'Djamma, tell him that if he does not go to the water at once, I've got a whole magazine ready for him.'

I shall never forget the expression of merciless ferocity in his bloodshot eyes. Nor shall I forget how the man replaced his dagger in its leather sheath and went to fetch the brackish water which the earth was sweating out drop by drop some hundred yards from our camp.

'They won't dare do anything tonight,' Djamma said. 'There are seven of us with firearms against three knives. But I should double the sentries, sir, all the same.'

I had finished my watch and was sleeping profoundly when Djamma awakened me.

'The Dankali warrior has left us,' he whispered. 'It's certainly to organise an ambush.'

Moussa had also disappeared.

But Moussa returned at dawn, as we were preparing to set out. I tried to get him to tell me where he had been. He would do nothing but smile.

We had no time to lose. If the fugitive Dankali had succeeded in joining a band of warriors from Lake Assal, many of whom had never seen a white face, we were bound to walk into a trap in the Gongouta defile. I put off explanations with Moussa, since my only concern was to get the caravan moving as fast as possible. The day's march was without incident.

On emerging from the gorges, we debouched on Lake Assal and its infernal splendour. All about it shone a saline quicksand with the dim glow of a dead star. Both men and animals become hopelessly bogged in it if they leave the track.

It was here we met some Danakils driving their half-wild camels. They were dressed in untanned hides, armed with lances and their long hair reached to their shoulders. I closed up my little band round Sultan Mohammed, as if about a hostage. But the warriors let us go by with an indifferent air. They had clearly not met our faithless guide.

The next day we came to the sea, where Monfreid was waiting with his boat.

It was only then that Moussa donned his bandage. At least that was what I thought it was at first. But, on looking closer, I realised that the curious substance which covered practically the whole of his left arm from the shoulder joint to the elbow consisted of thin strands of skin lying very close together.

I counted them automatically. There were twelve.

Suddenly, I understood. To the three barbaric trophies he had hitherto been wearing, Moussa had added the eight worn by his enemy. And the last, fresher and less shrivelled, was that of the Dankali warrior himself.

I confess that this realisation caused me no sense of horror whatever. I merely admired the moral arithmetic which allowed a conqueror to assume the insignia of valour of his fallen enemy.

'Every country has its own customs,' I thought as I gazed at Moussa's bright teeth.

I still thought so on the quay at Jibuti when I refused to take Moussa, despite all his supplications, to France. His body needed sun and black rocks, his muscles animal activity.

And what use could he have made of his twelve trophies in my employ in Paris?

For a moment I stroked the woolly head against my chest and then gently thrust him away.

The midnight mists lay over the banks of the Seine. A few rare lights seemed to be floating on a level with the stream. I suddenly shivered. Moussa was waiting for me in a fashionable restaurant on the Champs-Elysées.

I automatically began to walk in its direction. Then, I stopped dead in my tracks. I realised that I would not go, that I would not see Moussa again. It meant nothing to me to find out whether that black athlete had landed up in Paris in the second-hand clothes of a server of Turkish coffee because he had come to France as a stoker or followed another white master.

I went home, determined to preserve the memory of the Moussa of Daouenlé, of the Issa desert, of the nightly fires, the conqueror of the Dankali warrior, my childish protector, my ingenuous killer . . .

6
THE MUSCOVITE

As we approached the ramparts of San'a, a centaur emerged from the Western Gate, which was flanked by two massive towers. He was leaning over the withers of a splendid Arab horse and encouraging it with loud cries. He rode with such barbaric and impetuous speed that he seemed in danger of riding down our little caravan.

It was only at the very last moment that he turned his horse at full gallop to avoid us. We had scarcely time to see his flashing teeth and narrow Asiatic eyes before the horseman had disappeared.

Sheik Mohammed, whom the Imam, the ruler of the Yemen, had kindly given us as a guide, murmured respectfully: 'By Allah, it's the Muscovite!'

In other circumstances the man's appearance and the singular name Mohammed had given him would certainly have aroused our interest. But the fabulous route by which we had come had anaesthetised our capacity for astonishment. Moreover, the promise of what lay hidden behind the wild walls before us admitted of no delay.

With three friends, Lablache Combier, a Naval lieutenant, Emile Peyré, an Army medical officer and brother of the author of *l'Escadron Blanc*, and Gilbert Charles, the poet, I had left Hodeida, that fieriest of ports giving access to the low lands of the Yemen, otherwise known as Arabia Felix, a week before. We had at last received permission to go to San'a, the capital, which lies 9,000 feet up in the jebel on a lava plateau.

To the sure-footed, monotonous pacing of our mules, led by singing, bare-footed warriors whose long, coarse hair floated in the mountain wind, we had slowly made our way towards San'a. It was a wonderful climb through a miraculous landscape; cascades of red and grey rocks; chains of sharp peaks piercing the clouds that moved across their summits; red valleys, their sides carved into tiers;

barbaric, mysterious, fortified villages standing, like inaccessible nests, above high, steep precipices; and cities like the prows of ships, suspended above the abyss, cyclopean refuges over which the clouds and eagles floated.

Stage by stage, we had pursued this path of the Titans with incredulous wonder. It had a quality both of fable and epic, as it wound sublimely amid granite and bush and slag.

And now, at the end of our fantastic journey, the gates of San'a were opening before us.

Once again words are lacking to describe such ineffable enchantment.

The Thousand and One Nights, one's childhood dreams, every myth and imagining were here fulfilled and indeed surpassed by this city.

The narrow, high, grey houses, decorated with bright lime-wash and carved wood, looked like fortresses. Behind their walls, extensive gardens cast a mysterious shade. The water-wheels creaked a ceaseless song.

The suks and mosques, the streets and squares, were filled with a crowd in which mingled men from the mountains in short robes, sunburnt caravaneers in rags, Bedouins dressed in the skins of animals and warriors with flashing smiles. Against their robes shone the butts of guns and daggers set with precious stones. Their faces and gestures had a wild, free air, a refined yet animal grace.

'*Tang! Tang!* Make way! Make way!' cried the Imam's *askers* who were escorting us.

And we moved forward among the purest featured, most handsome faces produced by the Arab race in its cradle.

The house we had been given had three storeys. The carpets, hangings and silks were cut to pieces before our eyes and replaced by new ones. It was thus the Imam demonstrated the magnificence of his hospitality and that a house, like a woman, must be handed over virgin.

A fountain was singing in the garden which was full of fruit. Twelve warriors acted as our servants.

While our men were unloading the pack-mules, an old man entered the room. He was very tall, erect and handsome. He wore a blue turban. He saluted us with a noble gesture and said in perfect French: 'Welcome, gentlemen.'

He was Cadi Rahib, a former Turkish dignitary, who was now Foreign Minister to the Imam of the Yemen. He had been born in Constantinople and had served Abdul Hamid, the Red Sultan. As an attaché at the St Petersburg and Paris embassies, he had danced with the Empress of All the Russias and with Madame Steinhel, President Félix Faure's mistress. When the war, which was to dismember the huge Turkish Empire, broke out, he was governor of Hodeida. And when the Yemenites rebelled, he had seen which way the wind was blowing, and joined their side. Since he was the only man in the whole country who knew Europe, his betrayal gained him the post of Foreign Minister.

He had half a century of subtle intrigue, palace revolutions, amiable cruelty and unparalleled courtesy behind him.

Having inquired in his master's name if there was anything we required, he placed himself and his house at our service.

Next day, I returned Cadi Rahib's visit.

In the cool room into which a slave showed me, he was sitting talking to a man dressed in European clothes, but whose round face, shaved head, high cheek-bones and slit eyes betrayed Mongol origins.

I recognised the horseman who had emerged from the walls of San'a and galloped up to our caravan.

'Allow me to introduce M. Mourad, head of the Soviet Commercial Mission,' the master of the house said.

'Oh, so it's you they call the Muscovite?' I asked Cadi Rahib's guest. I spoke directly to him in Russian, feeling sure that my use of that tongue would amaze them. But neither the former governor of Hodeida nor the U.S.S.R. delegate showed any surprise at all. They both knew how to control their reactions.

Nevertheless, I thought Mourad seemed pleased when I complimented him on his horse and horsemanship.

'It was a present from the Imam,' he said. 'His Gracious Majesty gave me three pure-bred horses. I would be delighted if you would care to ride with me one day.'

Thereupon Mourad took his leave.

'A remarkable man,' Cadi Rahib said, nodding his head. 'He attends the five prayers in the principal mosque.'

This did not surprise me. I had already seen the two representatives of the Russian mission at Hodeida at work. They had known how to curry favour with the people, the princes, the merchants and the priests. Affable and cultivated, speaking perfect Arabic, fanatically devoted to their task in that infernal climate, they had succeeded in pushing their country's cigarettes, soap, paraffin and cloth on the Yemenite market. They talked with loving enthusiasm of the sterling they sent each quarter to Moscow to help with the first five-year plan. They themselves lived on very small salaries.

I told Cadi Rahib about them.

'Lenin is Allah and Stalin is his prophet,' he said thoughtfully.

I could not tell whether he was joking.

'I was born so to speak in the saddle,' Mourad said, when we had left the city walls. 'My father was a herdsman of horses in Turkestan. I followed the same trade till I was sixteen.'

We were riding side by side across the San'a plateau. The morning was crystal clear. White eagles were wheeling in the sky.

'It was there that the Revolution awakened me,' Mourad went on. 'I fought against the Whites because the Whites were the nobles and the rich. I was lucky during the civil war and became commissar of a cavalry regiment. I was present when Orenburg, on the Ural, was captured from Doutoff's Cossacks.'

'Orenburg,' I cried. 'That was where my mother was born.'

And I remembered my childhood, smart turn-outs of sledges, caravans, and Khirgiz camel-men who had journeyed across the steppes and deserts from Samarkand.

Mourad and I were so far away and so high up, indeed so cut off from the world, that we had for the moment forgotten all those tragedies and convulsions. And we talked of Orenburg simply as men who shared similar memories, recollections of the same landscapes.

'When Orenburg had been taken,' Mourad went on in a low voice, 'and the civil war was over, I went on courses to train me for work in the Orient. It was easier for me than for others because of my origins. I passed my examinations and was sent here.'

He absent-mindedly stroked his horse's mane and said: 'I owe everything to the Revolution.'

An hour later, reclining on a divan, we were watching a singing jet of water, which wavered and glistened, in a little pavilion the Imam had had built in the middle of a sweet-scented wood, on the slope of a mountain where there were many springs and streams.

Fragrant coffee, the best in the world, was steaming before us on a brass tray. Through the light, delicate arches of the interior courtyard we could see the heroic line of the mountains crowned with citadels.

'What a wonderful country!' I murmured, thinking aloud.

'Wonderful!' Mourad's voice echoed me.

He fell silent for a moment or two and then went on: 'And you have scarcely seen it. Even I, who have been working here for two years, know it so little. There are whole regions no traveller has ever entered.'

Mourad sat up. A curious eagerness glowed in his narrow eyes. His usually impassive face was illumined by an expression of violent enthusiasm, a stirring of his conquering, nomad blood. He cried: 'The city of Mareb, the antique and inviolable Mareb, the city that was Queen Saba's, belongs to the Imam. But it belongs to him only in name. His most stalwart warriors dare not risk their lives among the wild tribes that guard it.

'You have seen some of those indomitable Bedouins in the markets of San'a. The upper part of their bodies is naked, their hair is worn high on their heads and they carry their daggers in untanned leather sheaths. They look on Mareb as taboo. And anyone who tries to violate it is punished with death. Yet there huge temples sleep, and gold and marble statues rise from the sand . . .'

Mourad was talking as if hallucinated.

'I want to go there,' he went on. 'I've already managed to gain the support of certain chiefs. The date of my leave is drawing near. I shall not go back to Russia. I shall go to Mareb.'

He looked me straight in the eye and suddenly asked: 'You like horses, Arabia and adventure. Will you come with me?'

'Alas,' I replied, 'I must return to Europe soon. But if I can organise an expedition there, I accept with pleasure.'

We fell silent.

'To suggest such a journey together,' I said at last, 'you must feel a certain friendliness towards me, Mourad?'

'Much more than that,' Mourad replied, 'I only give my friendship in its entirety. I am a man of the Orient.'

Why did I ask him the following question? I do not know. Perhaps it was merely that I like to see into the depths of a man.

'If I committed a murder, would you hide me?' I asked.

Mourad gave a slight shrug and replied: 'Of course I would.'

'Even if the victim was your brother?'

'If you came to ask me asylum,' Mourad said, 'I would sleep across your door and they'd have to kill me before they could reach you.'

I knew I ought to be content with that answer. But I could not resist the temptation. Once again, I asked: 'But if the crime was not an ordinary criminal offence but a crime against the Soviet régime?'

His dark cheeks flushed slightly, his voice grew lower, but it was without hesitation or avoiding my eyes that the former herdsman of horses replied: 'I would give you up at once.'

We galloped back to San'a.

7
THE MAN WITH THE MONKEYS

IT WAS not without an obscure feeling of regret that I saw the white houses of Jidda approaching.

Yet no town on the whole Arabian coast is so beautiful seen from the sea. It lies in a vast semicircle along the shore and the coral banks are iridescent with a hundred delicate tints ranging gradually from purple to amethyst.

But though Jidda beckoned me, the ship slowly steaming towards it still had a certain attraction for me. You could not have said that it was distinguished for comfort or cleanliness. Indeed, it was an old tub belonging to the Indian line of Cowasdjee. It had no saloon or cabin. I had slept on a mattress on deck, my head against the rail. For food, I had had to rely on the rather limited ingenuity of my native servant.

But these material shortcomings were of little importance beside the continuous spectacle afforded by the five hundred Somali sinners on the lower deck, who were on a pilgrimage to Mecca. Their ablutions, their prayers and songs, the care they took of their white veils and the spiritual preparations to which they devoted themselves before landing on the sacred shore, the childish faith and candid joy of their expressions, their fear of contact with the infidels—the three British ship's officers and myself—all transformed in my eyes the broken-winded old beast of burden that had been sailing the Red Sea for forty years into a primitive ark filled with unsullied souls and naïve faces.

When you are living in a fairy tale, do eating badly and sleeping hard matter?

Having become a child myself, I saw the end of the fairy tale approach with melancholy.

Jidda prolonged it in a different way . . .

I was lucky enough to land there at the time of year Mecca

summons the faithful of the Moslem world to the great purification. From the first moment of landing at the port for the holy city, I found myself in fantastic surroundings. With their bags and suitcases, their poverty and wealth, their hundred languages and their hundred different casts of countenance, all those whom Mahomet's faith sustains and guides were there.

Important Moroccan caids with their motor-cars and their suites of secretaries and servants; Javanese as delicately slender as the statues in ancient temples; negroes from the heart of Africa; Abyssinians and Somalis; men from Bokhara in wonderfully embroidered robes; grave and wily Persians; Afghan warriors with hennaed beards; Mohammedan Indians—I cannot remember all the races the city, like a star flaming in the desert, attracted to itself.

And yet, strangely enough for an oriental crowd, there was no disorder among this errant mob, this frantic and ecstatic migration of a hundred races drawn from every point of the compass. There was a rough but effective organisation to deal with the distribution of these bewildered guests about the town. Using their whips when necessary, customs officers and police in ragged turbans formed the pilgrims into lines, inspected their luggage, extracted the appropriate dues, and led them to the inns and caravanserais.

I recognised in this the inflexible authority of the great Ibn Saud, the conqueror of Nejd and the Hedjaz.

The story of this chief of a small Wahabite tribe is well known. The Wahabites are fanatical warriors and strictly orthodox in religion. Little by little, Ibn Saud, by cunning as much as by courage, first became the ruler of Nejd and then turned his fanatical hordes against the rich, soft, corrupt Hedjaz. He defeated King Hussein, drove his troops into the sea and forced him to embark in a British warship. For Hussein was the official British protégé, or rather that of Colonel Lawrence, the uncrowned king of Arabia.

But in the shadow of Ibn Saud, the giant, there lurked another Englishman who had been following the fortunes of the Wahabite chief for many years and had foreseen and predicted his success.

The Colonial Office had refused to believe in it. It had complete faith in Lawrence's ideas.

Yet, Lawrence was wrong and it had to be admitted with astonishment that his obscure rival had been right. And the name of St John

Philby began to spread among officials in London, as it had already spread across the Arabian peninsula when the wild warriors of Nejd set up their spears on the shores of the Red Sea.

I was playing bridge at the Dutch Consulate. Some charming women were laughing and talking at the next table. I listened to their voices with pleasure. It was many months since I had seen or heard a European woman.

A record was playing slowly. It was a diplomatic privilege, for Wahabite law forbade music, singing and the use of tobacco throughout Ibn Saud's dominions. (As for adultery, even in Jidda, the port most accessible to western influence, it was punished by stoning.)

I was succumbing to a delightful sense of repose when a man came into the room. His face had a curiously stimulating effect on me. I noticed only a short, red, slightly satanic beard; and his eyes of intense, violent and violet blue. They shone with so hard a light and had such a quiet and moving audacity that once seen they could never be forgotten.

He introduced himself: 'St John Philby.'

And he asked me to go to see him the day after tomorrow.

That day, the *khamsin*, known elsewhere as the *simoun* or the sand wind, was blowing through the town. The air was thick and yellow. It was extraordinarily difficult to breathe. One's whole body was covered with a sticky moisture. The heat was suffocating and intolerable.

After the inferno of the streets and alleys, Philby's house seemed to me a delightful oasis. It was a splendid building, with big, high rooms, thick walls and with its enclosed courtyards and crenellations had something both of a palace and a fortress. A wide terrace gave on to the sea.

It was there that I found Philby, in spite of the ceaselessly whirling dust. He was surrounded by a dozen little monkeys. Two of them were perched on his shoulders. Three others were clinging to his knees with their intelligent little heads against his chest. Philby continued petting them throughout our interview.

'I like this wind,' he said, his strange violet eyes fixed on the yellow cloud oscillating heavily beneath the invisible sky. 'It reminds me of the desert and my youth.'

He then told me how he had left the Indian Civil Service for Arabia, and how he had followed Ibn Saud's standards from the Persian Gulf to the Red Sea. He also told me that he preferred Arabs to Christians and that he was shortly to become a convert to Islam.

'The only reason I have waited so long,' he said, 'is because I do not wish to treat these matters lightly. The desert and the men of the desert have taught me to be serious.'

He also said: 'I shall always defend my friends, even against England if necessary.'

Was he sincere? Or was he merely concealing the fact that he was an agent of the Intelligence Service, as has so often been claimed?

I had no evidence either way. But what was clear was that he belonged to the race of great adventurers, the lovers of open spaces, the mystics of the unknown and of discovery. His desire for these things was insatiable. The years spent in tents and under the flaming sun, the years of caravans, of hunger, thirst and pain, did not suffice him.

When I told him how I envied so complete a knowledge of Arabia, he cried: 'Don't say that! I still have everything to learn.'

And his violet eyes shone with an almost intolerable light.

'Do you know,' he went on, 'that in Southern Arabia, between the Yemen, the Nedj and the Hadramaut, there is a huge territory of which nothing is known? Do you realise that: nothing! The most enthusiastic travellers and the most daring Bedouin don't know it. It belongs to nobody. Terror and mystery are its masters. It is called Rob-el-Khali, the empty land.

'There are a thousand legends concerning it. It is said that white Arabs with blue eyes live in its centre. People say that Jewish tribes fled there in the time of Saul and still exist.

'All that is known about this desert is this: the tribes who take their herds to pasture on the borders of Rob-el-Khali have the strongest and fleetest camels in the world. It is because these Bedouin drive their female camels during the rutting season into the unknown desert where they are served by the wild camels.'

Philby took a deep breath and suddenly got to his feet. The little monkeys did not lose their balance and clung to him. Philby led me into a bare room off the terrace. There was nothing in it but two long chests worked in the Arab manner.

'I shall take these when I go into the Rob-el-Khali,' my host said. 'These chests exactly fit my camels' pack-saddles.'

He raised a lid. There were compartments for everything, from food to scientific instruments.

'When do you expect to set out?' I asked.

'*Inch 'Allah!*' St John Philby replied.

Allah was merciful. A few years later a book appeared under the signature of the man with the monkeys. It recorded the crossing of the Rob-el-Khali.

8
A WOMAN FROM THE PROVINCES

BEFORE the last war, there was a bar in the Rue Fromentin kept by a man who, though still young, had been a very rich business-man in Moscow. Now, from behind his counter, he watched his nightly customers with an attentive eye. They were nearly all Russian. Musicians, singers out of a job, people who had finished work, newspaper sellers, night-birds short of cash, came here to eat caviar and cheap pirojki, and drink vodka at modest cost.

The sound of a guitar and battered voices was often to be heard, for music and singing are so very much a part of the Russian's very fibre that even those who had played and sung all night to earn their livings began again immediately afterwards for their own pleasure.

There were often fights, for a good deal of drinking went on and nerves were taut among people on whom memory acted like an open wound. Strange ghosts wandered there, their faces bearing the traces of poverty, heedlessness and former splendour. In short, it was an extraordinary enough place and, at one time, I used to go there every night.

One of the habitués who interested me most was a Cossack called Stiopa. Not that he had much to say for himself. Indeed, he had no conversation at all. He was always drunk. But it was precisely his silence, his incapacity for thought or memory and his animality which attracted me.

He had a way of making his entrance, his astrakhan cap over one ear and showing wild, curly red hair, of placing his hands on his hips over which a crimson tunic fitted tightly, of looking round with a glance which was at once drunken, bold and cruel, which compelled one to recognise that he was a man born for war and orgy, for vaulting on to a horse and for dancing to the sound of frenzied cries, for the simplest and most violent forms of lust and for easily accepted death.

Habitués of the little bar had told me that, in 1914, he had belonged to the crack squadrons, known as the wild squadrons, that he had charged barbed wire on horseback, and during the Revolution had served with many leaders of bands and had massacred with Makhno.

What did this horseman with no other law but that of battle, carnage and orgy do in Paris? On what did he live?

No one knew, but each evening he kicked the door of the bar open, his red mouth wide in a ferocious, silent smile, went straight to the counter where he drank off two glasses of vodka, and then sat down at a table where he stood drinks to people whose faces he liked. He never left till dawn, terribly drunk and his hand on his dagger. It was a miracle he had never drawn it. And lucky too. I had seen him fight with bare hands, and in every gesture there had been the lust to kill.

One night, when he had stood me a drink as usual, and a guitarist who had played for Rasputin was talking to me about that lubricious, crafty, obscene and fascinating Siberian Moujik, we saw a woman come in. Her appearance was unusual for that place and attracted everyone's attention. She was wearing a worn coat whose cloth and cut were seldom to be seen in Paris. Her skirt was much longer than fashion decreed. Beneath her shabby, tasteless hat, she wore a thick bun.

And this woman, who seemed like a fish out of water in Montmartre, came and sat at our table. Stiopa, the Cossack, was the only one of us not to be surprised. He signed to her to sit beside him.

He then continued to drink in silence. The woman waited for him till morning without uttering a word, or having a drink. They went off together.

I had plenty of opportunity for observing this strange creature. In spite of her graceless clothes, I noticed that she was still young and had great charm due to the tender expression of her mouth, the grave sadness and, when she looked at Stiopa, the expression of love evident in her regular features.

She returned the next day and, by the way she said to me before sitting down by Stiopa: 'I beg your pardon, Monsieur,' I realised that she was French and well-educated.

I felt a certain uneasiness, indeed almost a sense of dread. What was the relationship between these two? Between the cut-throat with the silent, terrible laugh, and this woman from the provinces with her reserve, her good manners and her gentleness?

No one could give me the slightest information. No one had ever seen the woman before the previous evening. And when my curiosity, encouraged by alcohol and lack of sleep, eventually brought me to the pitch of asking Stiopa directly who his companion was, he merely shrugged his wide, hard shoulders and said: 'Her name's Berthe.'

Hearing her name uttered by that barbarous voice, the woman's face quivered and then her whole body. Her expression, normally so decent and so modest, assumed a sort of secret excitement, a voluptuous subjection, before becoming wholly immobile once more.

From then on, I saw her every night. The group who joined Stiopa paid as little attention to Berthe as he did himself. She sat there, neither drinking nor eating, understanding nothing of what was said, until the moment came when the drunken Cossack wished to leave. Then she followed him.

Little by little, I got on terms with Berthe, despite her natural shyness and the profound and inevitable embarrassment the place caused her. I was the only person who could speak fluently the language of her country, which seemed so far away amid these high cheek-boned faces, these Cossack clothes, the Tziganes, and the foreign food and drink.

After a week, Berthe was quite willing to talk to me. And the better I got to know her, the more surprised I became. She was not only well brought up, but she was subtle and cultivated. She would make remarks about literature and music which revealed not only extensive knowledge but discriminating taste. And beside her sat this man with his cut-throat head, his grimace, his killer's hand and his perpetual drunkenness . . .

Though I did not dare question Berthe directly, I tried by various subterfuges and suggestions to discover her origins and the secret of her liaison. But, as soon as she felt my curiosity awakening, however little, Berthe withdrew into herself with something approaching panic.

Yet, there came a time, as inevitably happens during those sleepless nights which exhaust the nerves and cause feverish lips to utter the most secret and repressed of confidences, when Berthe talked.

Stiopa, the Cossack, always arrived first. His mistress joined him only rather late at night.

He usually came alone. Yet, one night, accompanying Stiopa's ritual kick against the bar door, there was a gay little laugh. There was a young woman with him. She was dressed as a Cossack. I recognised her as a dancer from a Russian nightclub nearby.

'I'm in the money,' Stiopa cried. 'This is a party.'

He invited everyone present to as much vodka or red wine as they could drink. The whole climate changed quickly. The guitars—there were always several about—began to play of their own accord. Stiopa sent for an accordion and began to play too.

It was as if this man, who could not talk, had found his means of expression. All his innate savagery, restrained by the customs of a great city, all his thirst for the open spaces, for adventure and battle, all his wild soul and primitive heart sounded through the notes of the accordion, as he squeezed and released it with his terrible hands. It was a paean of naked instinct.

It was an extraordinary sight to see Stiopa, in his red tunic and shining boots, erect, on tip-toe, his wild body supported, as it were, by the waves of music, and his accordion crying under his fingers like an avowal. The whole room fell under the sway of his forceful ascendancy till the instrument ceased singing.

It was only then I saw that Berthe was present. I scarcely recognised her. It was as if Stiopa's delirious music had sculpted this woman from the provinces a new face. Her eyes were wide and moist, her cheeks were aflame and her lips were parted in a troubled smile. She was breathing with the difficult respiration of a woman subject to desire.

Suddenly she turned pale. Stiopa was kissing the girl dressed as a Cossack on the mouth.

He then threw a thousand-franc note to a violinist, who had come to drink a brandy during an interval of the band, and ordered him to play a *lesghinka*. Scarcely had the first chords of the Caucasian dance rung out, when the dancer was whirling among the tables. The guitars joined in. Everyone began shouting and Stiopa partnered her in the dance.

It was at this point I felt a quivering shoulder against mine and heard Berthe murmur: 'Tell me, Monsieur, you know him, is he going to leave me for that girl? I'm not the right woman for him, I know. I was married to a professor in the East. He came to work for us as a gardener last summer. I went off with him. He wanted to enlist in the Foreign Legion because he had no money. I managed to earn some. I go every day to a . . . brothel. He doesn't need much to come here and stand drinks . . . We scarcely speak to each other. He only knows about ten words of French, but I understand him so well. He's a savage, a child. I know very well he'll leave me one day, but not yet . . . please, beg him, not yet.'

When Stiopa had spent the money an American had paid him for kidnapping his little girl from his divorced wife, he went off to the Legion.

Berthe no longer came to the Rue Fromentin.

My curiosity about the night-life of Paris soon led me elsewhere.

Two or three years later, a lecture tour took me from one big town to another through the French provinces. My subject was Soviet literature. There were always many students and university teachers in the audience.

The last town of my tour was Strasbourg.

I knew my lecture by heart, having delivered it a dozen times in the last few days. And yet, on this occasion, the opening words escaped me.

A couple had just taken their seats in the front row, immediately opposite the platform. I recognized the woman as Berthe.

There could be no doubt of it. Our eyes had met and she had greeted me with a brief nod.

Berthe, Stiopa's mistress, the prostitute from the brothels, was here in this peaceful and studious assembly!

With some difficulty I set about saying what I had to say. Then, the mechanism began to function. The familiar words followed each other of their own accord.

From time to time, taking advantage of a pause, toying with a glass of water, I looked rapidly and furtively at the couple. But it was no longer Berthe who was compelling my attention, but the man sitting beside her.

Was he her husband? It certainly seemed so. There is a comportment, a mutuality, a habit between two bodies, between two beings, which cannot deceive one. And then, in the Rue Fromentin, the night of the wild accordion, Berthe had said: 'My husband, a professor in the East.'

Little by little, secret glance by secret glance, I took in his features: square, clean-cut, a wide serene forehead and a singularly well-shaped mouth. He was listening intently but without effort as only men engaged in high intellectual work are able to do.

After the lecture, students came up to ask me questions. When we had done, the hall was empty.

As I was leaving, an usher handed me a note. It was from Berthe and read: 'I have concealed nothing from him. Life has returned to what it was before.'

What it was before—that is to say, ordered, protected, with dinner-parties among the staff, visits to other husbands and wives, concerts, plays by touring companies, lectures . . .

Who could have imagined that in such a life there had been so incredible an interlude, so crazy an escapade, such a flight into hell?

9
A PRINCE

THE night was almost over when we came out of the last bar. A cold rain was falling on Berlin. In this lost and dangerous district you had to walk a long way in search of a taxi. We were all three soaked to the skin when we at last found a driver who would agree to take us.

My friend, André Daven, who before the advent of Hitler directed the production of French films at the UFA, said: 'Come and have a night-cap with me. It'll warm us up.'

The taxi dropped us in a residential district. It had wide grass avenues and silence lay over it like a pall. The block of flats in which Daven lived was new, luxurious and had, like most blocks in Berlin, no porter.

Standing in the rain, my friend impatiently sought for his key. One pocket, another, trousers, coat, waistcoat, overcoat, once, twice, a third time . . . Daven swore. There could be no doubt of it: he had forgotten his keys.

What should we do? This district, slumbering so luxuriously, was as innocent of taxis as was the poverty-stricken district we had just left. We were exhausted. It was raining harder than ever.

Then, our companion, who had been our guide and protector among the low haunts we had visited, said quietly: 'Don't worry, I'll fix it.'

By the light from a lamp-post, which looked ghostly in the rain, we saw he was holding a metal ring to which various little instruments were attached. He went to the door. It opened without a sound.

Our companion was Albert, prince of the German fraternity of thieves. How I came to know him is of no importance. The essential fact was that, like many bad hats in every latitude, he had soon come to trust me and had become my firm friend. Like the others, he had no doubt divined that by nature I tend less to judge men, whoever they may be, than to approach them and learn about their lives without prejudices.

And Albert the Hanoverian's life, by its restlessness, its ups and downs, its violence—even its viciousness, if you like—was not one to leave me indifferent.

Albert came from an honest middle-class Hanoverian family. His father had been a captain in the regular army when a serious riding accident put an end to his career. Reduced to living on a modest pension, the invalid concerned himself with every detail of his son's education. As a result, Albert's childhood and boyhood were passed amid money difficulties and barrack discipline. He acquired excellent manners but a profound distaste for poverty and constraint.

The First World War resolved these contradictions. Albert joined up at seventeen. Owing to his temperament and heredity, he fought well. He was wounded, decorated, and returned to the front. At the Armistice, he was a lieutenant.

His destiny then assumed that anarchic shape for which the whole of Germany, in 1920, set the example. An American woman made it possible for him to live luxuriously. He was blond, had charming though virile features, and his greenish eyes were full of audacity.

He then commanded a *corps franc* in Upper Silesia during the period before the plebiscite. It required courage and ruthlessness. Albert had enough of both.

Unfortunately, as in all secret work, he had considerable sums of money at his disposal. He was unable to resist the temptation of making off with the cash. Albert then lived the life of a rich tourist. The Italian lakes, Venice, Naples and Monte Carlo diminished his resources. Paris was his ruin.

He frequented Montmartre and its doubtful bars, and became a receiver. This cost him two years in Fresnes prison.

'I had time to learn French properly,' he would say with a childish smile which showed his admirably white and regular teeth.

On coming out of prison, he was deported and returned to Germany, where he went to live in Berlin. It was there I met him, at the time when the last free elections, those which preceded Hitler's advent to power, were taking place.

From the moment I got to know Albert, I forgot all about politics. For he led me into a realm even the possibility of whose existence I had never suspected.

This realm was called the *Unterwelt*. And this underworld, in comparison to the French *milieu*, was like an organised, disciplined, strictly hierarchical army compared to bands of irregulars. It had its leaders and its laws, its routines and its sanctions, its great festivals and its corporative mourning.

The reality to which Albert initiated me was wholly improbable. The German need for discipline was so strong that even people living outside the law, who rebelled by their actions against the established order, at once formed themselves into an organisation, made their own rules, insisted on a discipline, banners and officers, and happily bent their necks beneath a new yoke.

'Thieves, sharpers, pimps, robbers with violence and killers are all organised here,' Albert said proudly. 'They are elected and grouped into leagues, unions and syndicates. And then one has to obey! We have to help each other, and come punctually to meetings; if you don't, you get heavily fined. This is what gives us our power, as discipline has always given Germany hers.'

He spoke seriously, excitedly, as one convinced. He also showed me his union badge which he was wearing *openly* in his button-hole; and this union comprised, as he himself told me, only burglars and pimps.

And this badge possessed prodigious power. Thanks to his little brass button, Albert was at home everywhere, in nightclubs and great hotels, in luxurious establishments of the international class as well as in homosexual bars and the lowest brothels.

During the few weeks I followed his activities, Albert moved in every kind of circle, for he was peddling drugs. I saw many a bemedalled commissionaire, and the manager of many fashionable restaurants, bow low before his badge and carry out his behests. They too belonged to the *Unterwelt* and it was the *Unterwelt* which, by threatening the establishments they had selected with reprisals, had obtained their jobs for them. And they knew Albert to be one of the princes of the underworld.

He also looked the part. His clothes, shoes and hats had a sober elegance. His ties and shirts, and the few jewels he wore, all came from the best shops. Nothing flashy. Nothing that was not in the best of taste. In this, as well as in his language and gestures, Albert's education was apparent.

He often carried a brief-case under his arm. In it were cocaine, morphine and heroin. But even the brief-case was an addition to his personality and gave him the appearance of being an important engineer or a young leader of industry.

Nevertheless, his elegance and love of luxury did not prevent his being at ease in the most sordid places and being received in them on familiar terms. He had contacts everywhere. The ramifications of his union, or of similar ones, were everywhere, and the tentacles of the *Unterwelt* widespread.

I accompanied Albert all over the place, to the Alexanderplatz, the Silesian station, the Northern and Eastern districts, suburbs of greater Berlin, in a smart little American car which a Pitsburgh businessman had given his mistress, a hostess in one of the most fashionable nightclubs in the Kurfurstendam.

There were sinister streets, haunting in their dull regularity. There were low bars where criminals gathered, and damp, dank cellars where heavy, massive men with knotted muscles, bestial faces and terrifying hands held sway, stranglers, killers who never carried a pistol and almost never a knife, for their hands sufficed them.

They seemed to belong to another century and not to this in which the criminal of the modern city knows so well how to use automatic weapons. I often felt, in these places and with these people, that Albert's friends were like the criminals depicted by Hugo in *Les Misérables* or Eugène Sue in *Les Mystères de Paris.*

Yet, Berlin was not the background to the most astonishing scene I owed to Albert.

'The president of our Union is sending me to Hamburg,' Albert said one morning. 'I've got to sell some diamonds stolen by one of our members. He's in prison. The stones are too hot here. It shouldn't take more than four days. Will you come?'

It was thus I got to know Hamburg with its splendid old houses, its marine atmosphere, its canals and lake-side squares. I also got to know the lights, chandeliers and band of Sankt Pauli, known to sailors throughout the world; the refuges of professional beggars and pickpockets; the extraordinary Court of Miracles; and the cellars of the Chinese.

Albert managed his business promptly. The day after our arrival the diamonds were sold for a good price through a Syrian receiver.

'I've got two days' holiday,' Albert said gaily. 'I'll send for my princess.'

I thought he meant by this a charming young girl who 'worked' for him at Ciro's. But when we went to fetch her at the airport, a tall, heavy, haughty woman of forty appeared.

I do not know whether the title Albert gave her was correct, but there was no doubt that she belonged to the German aristocracy. Her stiffness, her manners, her language and even her prejudices were all guarantees of her origin. She must once have been very beautiful. Her face, in spite of the make-up and an unhealthy puffiness, still showed it. Her eyes seemed fixed and rather haggard, the eyes of a neurasthenic or of someone obsessed.

What was Albert's hold over her? Was it physical or due to the drugs he sold her? I think probably both. But the latter was certainly the stronger. Like so many addicts, this woman, in spite of her pride, had become her supplier's slave.

That very evening, Albert took the princess to the Chinese. I must do him the justice of recording that it was not he who suggested the expedition and that he even tried to dissuade her from it. But she overcame his scruples with an appropriate sum of money.

Nevertheless, Albert was nervous when we turned into a dark, dirty, ill-paved alley near the harbour.

'I don't like these yellow men,' he admitted. 'They live in their dens like wolves. They trust no one. I've sometimes bought opium from them, but the deals were made in the docks at night. I've never visited them. Strangers who enter their dens often disappear without trace. No, I don't like these yellow men.'

The sordid street in which we were had basement areas on each side, so that the façades of the houses were prolonged below the level of the cobbles. There were stairs leading down and these we took.

'That's where they live,' Albert murmured, pointing to a series of closed doors. Not a sound or a gleam of light came from them.

Albert knocked on one of the doors. There was no reply. Nor was he any luckier when he tried the others. He then took from his pocket the little outfit he had used on André Daven's flat, selected an instrument and put it into the lock. It yielded softly.

We went in and the door closed behind us.

I was immediately aware of China, its smell, its climate, its secret.

There were a maze of passages, a smell of dried fish, of exotic spices, a swarm of yellow faces and, above all, the suave, acrid odour of opium.

The owner of the place, a tall Manchu with a hard, false face, asked curtly: 'Who are you and what do you want?'

'The lady wants to smoke,' Albert said. 'She'll pay well.'

The Manchu looked the princess up and down. Her appearance and the jewellery which, in spite of Albert's warnings, she had insisted on wearing, presumably set his doubts at rest.

'Very well,' he said.

We followed him across a big hall in which people were playing mah-jong, then through a series of passages off which led dark side-turnings.

'These houses might have been excavated by a mole,' Albert whispered. 'I'm sure one can go to the waterside by these underground passages. It's a real trap.'

We finally reached a small cellar with divans round the walls. On most of them Chinese were smoking in silence. You could hear nothing but the sizzling of the pellets and the rather hoarse breathing of the smokers.

The princess lay down beside a tray and let loose her long, heavy fair hair. A young Chinese crouched beside her and began to manipulate the drug.

Thus began a fantastic night whose elements were silence, the odour of opium, yellow faces in a warm twilight and the sense of being in a completely strange environment. All the demons of China seemed to have gathered round the fair hair spread out like a strange metal in an enchanted cavern.

Time passed insensibly and became measureless. Moreover, in the depths of that labyrinth there was neither night nor day.

Every now and then Albert slept. I, too, lost all sense of reality. Everything became a dream: the smokers leaving to go to work; the hushed life of the labyrinth; the arrival of other yellow faces.

The princess was still lying there, inhaling the smoke of the opium.

By our watches we knew that a night and a day and another night had passed thus.

'I must go back to Berlin,' Albert said.

The princess did not seem to have heard him. Prayers, threats, nothing was of any use. We had to leave without her.

A fortnight later, having penetrated other secrets of the *Unterwelt*, sometimes at the cost of a broken head, I was leaving Berlin. Albert came with me to the station.

'Give my respects to the princess,' I said laughingly.

He shook his head with a sombre expression.

'She hasn't come back,' he said.

'What do you mean? A crime . . .'

'No, not even that. Our members in Hamburg have made inquiries. She's never left the damned cellar. She's sleeping with the owner, the big Chinese. She pays him with her jewels.'

10

THE GOATEE

ONE night a little before Christmas, it occurred to me to go and have a drink with Hippolyte.

I knew both the bar and the time at which he was sure to be found there, for Hippolyte, during the course of his idle and mysterious day, had certain fixed ports at which nothing could prevent his calling. Indeed, before I even pushed the door open, I saw, through the misty glass pane of winter, his huge figure standing at the counter.

He had adopted his usual attitude and was standing at the centre of the bar as if that commanding position were the only one proper for him. His hands were in his pockets and he appeared not to notice anyone. Besides, his head was so high above other people's that disdain was natural to him.

I stood there a few seconds before going in. I like men and places for the reveries they arouse. And in this respect nothing could have been more effective than the spectacle before me.

The damp, misty pane through which I was watching the bar lent him a secret, distorted halo. I knew that the people who gathered here lived dangerous, violent, treacherous lives. I knew that Hippolyte dominated them all. He had great strength, a sort of sombre courage and a determination that was no particular merit to him since it was derived from cast-iron muscles and a temperament wholly peculiar to himself.

He had known the stews and prisons of the world. He had fought for himself, his women, his friends and, on occasion, his country which he unwittingly loved. All this gave him a sort of magnetism; and it was so powerful that passers-by hastening along the little Montmartre street, in which I now stood in the cold, could not resist slowing their pace as they passed the bar and taking a look at the solid, motionless colossus that was Hippolyte standing at the counter.

I opened the door. Though he appeared to notice nothing in his monumental indolence, he saw me at once. It did not surprise me. I was used to his perpetual and unconscious watchfulness.

Hippolyte turned his square chin towards me. The layer of fat covering it could not conceal its tragic characteristics of obstinacy and pride. He did not remove his hands from his pockets but I was aware, from a sort of gleam in his sultry eyes, that he was pleased to see me.

'What'll you have, my lad?' he asked, with no more emphasis than if we had parted that very morning, when in fact I had not seen him for months.

The men drinking at the counter had clearly no wish to make room for me. For them, it was not so much a matter of convenience or mere casualness as of honour. Nevertheless, at the effectionate tone in which Hippolyte addressed me—and one had to know him well to distinguish the shade of difference in his impassive voice—they moved aside without a murmur to allow me to join him. Indeed, to show their deference, they even made a little space round us.

Hippolyte appreciated this sort of homage. He became slightly more animated and his face, still as a bronze statue's, came alive for a moment.

'I'm glad you came,' he said. 'I was bored.'

He fell silent. I drank the drink he had ordered for me. With a mere glance, he ordered another and took some notes from his pocket. I made no attempt to argue. Hippolyte did not permit one to pay when in his company.

'I'll take you to dine at a quiet little place,' he said.

In fact, the place was as quiet as you could want. It was a room behind a wine-bar where normally only the owner and his servant ate. They had scarcely finished their meal when we arrived.

'We'll leave the place to you,' the man said to Hippolyte, with that mixture of respect and fear my companion always aroused. 'Jeanne will prepare you a nice dish of tripe.'

'I shall enjoy that,' Hippolyte replied.

Then, as if these few words had been a priceless gift, he withdrew his attention from the man.

We sat down opposite each other. It was very hot in the little room. Next door, we could hear slow working-men's voices, and the clink of glasses against the zinc of the counter.

'I like that,' Hippolyte muttered with a gesture of despair. 'I'm getting old.'

'You're not yet forty,' I said.

He shrugged. It was a familiar gesture. When Samson pulled down the bronze columns, I thought, he must have suffered from the same terrible impatience.

'I learnt in the army that the years of campaigning count double,' Hippolyte went on. 'You can see, therefore, how many years mine add up to. You see it's like this. When holidays come along nowadays, I'm bored. I'd rather there were no more Christmas and no New Year. What's the use of them? People look as if they could have the moon for the asking. But none of it means anything to me any more. And I'm bored.'

The servant came in with a steaming dish. Hippolyte ate without haste and in silence.

I liked Hippolyte's silences. There was a sort of animal transparency about them that made them easy to tolerate. While they lasted, you could see his thought wandering across his usually expressionless face like some clumsy insect. And after even an hour, he always took up the conversation again at the precise phrase at which it had ceased and, since he was incapable of discussion, he recounted a fact. And the fact invariably turned out to be an astonishing story.

Hippolyte said not a word till we reached the coffee.

'I'm bored,' he then went on. 'And yet, I've got as much money as I want' (indeed, his pockets were always stuffed with money, though I never knew where it came from) 'and more women than I can do with. And you saw, when you knew me at Beirut, what that means to me. I ought to be happy. Well, the fact is I'm bored. Suppose I tell you I'm always thinking of things that happened twenty years ago! And I turn them over in my mind like an old man regretting them. The things that happened in the days when I was unfortunate. For instance, all today I haven't been able to rid my mind of the curious recollection of a certain Christmas, a very odd Christmas.

'The trouble is that, with you, I shall have to start right at the beginning. You don't know about life. You don't understand unless things are explained to you. Light a cigarette and sit still, and I'll tell you about it.

'At the time I'm telling you about, I wasn't much more than twenty. I was as slender as a dancer and, I can tell you, there aren't all that many good-looking youngsters today as well-built as I was. You know Louis and you can ask him. We're the same age. In those days he was called the Corsican, and I was called the Algerian, because of where we were born. I'd already been about a bit: Morocco, Alexandria, Palestine. And I'd taken some hard knocks in all of them. I arrived in Paris in a rage and, as you can imagine, I didn't want to do any military service. I wanted enough to eat and to have a bit of fun. Things went badly with me till the day I met Juliette.

'I must tell you things as they were: it wasn't I but she who had the idea of the trick. Since I was a good-looking youngster, the South Americans who came to Paris for new blood would come to me to find them women to take away. They'd pay two or three thousand francs per head. But I was young and bungling, and to tell you the truth I didn't like the job. It was Juliette who persuaded me. I gave her to the first purchaser, merely with her shirt and a tattered old dress. He dressed her like a queen and took her to Bordeaux. But there she slipped through his fingers and returned to me. We arranged it between us. I sold her five times. She was vicious and always managed to get back to me. The traffickers couldn't go to the police. As for seeking me out, I was dangerous. And they knew it.

'I had a good life all that summer. The only thing is, one always has to pay for these irregularities.

'I was given away to the police as a defaulter from military service. By whom? A South American? By Juliette who was in love with someone else and was afraid of me? I don't know.

'One way or another, I was picked up and sent off to the battalions in Africa. I don't know what the journey's like today. The army's become softer than it was in the days I'm talking of; and it's just as well, because I'm damned if the boys you see about today could take what we could take.

'On the train and in the ship, we were chained in pairs. You can imagine what that was like. Herded like animals, you couldn't move without hearing those damned irons ring and tugging at your neighbour. And he couldn't move without making your ankle ring.

'If you had a good comrade on your chain, it was less bad, but he had to be a really good one. And I had no luck. I recognised the man I was paired with at once. He was a tall, thin, tow-headed, dirty fellow, whom I'd constantly seen about in Montmartre. His was the worst of all trades, a beggar's. He used to beg with a false blind eye which he fixed with some ointment.

'Beggars disgust me more than anything. They're not men. And I had to be tied to this one for weeks and weeks. For, I must tell you, we didn't travel quickly.

'In spite of what I thought, I behaved very well to him. Don't imagine I was kind, I'm not kind. I'm correct, which is not the same thing. In misfortune, one must have principles. The beggar was a companion in misfortune, he had no money, nothing to buy food with. I had a little and shared it with him.

'It being his nature to extend his hand, he made no difficulties about accepting it. He behaved pretty decently and I didn't regret what I was doing for him.

'I won't bore you with the disembarkation and the start of our military training. I've even forgotten the name of the village to which we were first taken. I've seen so many of those places since that I don't know which it was.

'We were not too unhappy. I behaved well. And I've always liked arms. Besides, at that time, I didn't much mind what I ate or where I slept. All I asked was not to be shut in all the time. As a result of my good conduct, I was allowed out two or three times a week to go and have a drink and a woman.

'All might have gone well and I might perhaps have served my time quietly—I say perhaps, because one can never be sure of oneself, can one?—if one evening . . .

'Wait a minute, I realise I've forgotten to tell you that my chain-companion, the beggar, had been made a corporal. Considering the sort of bum-sucker he was, there was nothing surprising about that. Well, one evening when I was going down to the town, he was on the barrack guard.

'I said to him: "Be seeing you, lad . . ." And I went out.

'I'd only gone a step or two when I heard him shout: "Come here, Private Hippolyte!"

'I turned, thinking he was joking. I saw he was furiously angry. He started shouting: "Can't you salute? About turn, and get back into barracks!"

'I'd been quite still till then. Now, I became angry. Luckily for me, however, I saw red to such an extent that I never thought of the bayonet at my belt. I hit him with my fist. There he was on the ground and his filthy beggar's face had a whining expression on it again. He thought he could pull his stripes over a chap who'd shared his bread with him.

'I had no time to hit him again. The guard jumped on me.

'Cells, court-martial and the rest. My period of service was extended and I was sent to a penal battalion in the desert, building roads. Before leaving, I told a friend of mine, called Achille, the whole story. He was an old soldier, and had guts if anyone had. A fortnight after I'd left, the beggar was found in an alley with a bayonet in his back. Since it was his own, no one ever knew who had made use of it.

'I only heard this later, after what I'm going to tell you about—and this is what's worrying me. It's taken me a long time to reach it, but I couldn't tell you about it without telling you something of what had happened before and of the sort of chap I was.

'Well, there I was in the desert, and I found out what it meant to be really miserable. And you can believe me, when I tell you so. During the day, the heat was enough to drive you mad, and at night it was cold enough to freeze your stomach for you. We slept on the stones we broke during the day; we were given filth to eat; and we drank water that had to be fetched from kilometres away and arrived putrid in stinking goatskins. If you stopped work for a second you were hit with a rifle-butt, and there were Senegalese all around just waiting to shoot you for the least fault. It was a life, I can tell you.

'In spite of everything, I bore it all without flinching. And I hope you realise that it was not fear of a bullet that kept me quiet. I bore it all because we had a most unusual lieutenant.

'He was a Corsican and was called Salvi. In general, Corsicans are good or bad all through. This one was good all through. He was fair, straightforward and understood men. A proper commander.

When he asked a man: 'Everything all right?' there was not one among us, however browned off, however mutinous, who would not reply: "Quite all right, sir."

'To what was this due? I'm not clever enough to be able to say. He was short, lean, had sad eyes and a little beard. It was the beard I liked him for. When someone had to be punished, he had a way of twisting it which showed he disliked the business. I can assure you that men who are in a position to punish and dislike doing it are rare.

'I had spent a month in the desert. It was getting towards the end of December. Then a funny thing happened. The men with me were not much given to sentiment. Yet they all began to think of Christmas, and its accompanying rejoicings. They became uneasy, sad, sickened. Some—and not always the youngest—wept. I said nothing. I clenched my teeth. But it was having its effect on me, too. It became worse every day. In the end I fell into a deep depression.

'You chaps don't know what the *cafard* in the desert is like. It's the *cafard* of the sun and of the sand. There's no end to it and no way out. You go mad, you fall into the deepest depression, there's no other possible description of it.

'Then, you think up the most terrible thing you can do, but the most terrible against yourself. You don't know you're thinking it up, but someone, inside you, is thinking it up for you.

'On the morning of 24 December—you see how I remember the date—our section was inspected, as it was every morning, by Lieutenant Salvi. I looked at him and I liked him and his little beard more than ever. And suddenly I said to myself: 'I'll pull his goatee for him.'

'And you needn't believe me, but I didn't hesitate a second. I stepped out of the ranks, I went up to him, and I pulled out a good handful of hairs.

'I shall always remember the lieutenant's eyes. They were sadder than usual, but not at all angry. It was my comrades who were angry instead. He didn't have to utter a word. They beat me up so violently that I lost consciousness.

'I came to in a "silo." Don't you know what that is? Well, imagine a sort of well, dug fairly deep, full of scorpions and insects, just large enough to allow you to roll yourself into a ball. In the desert, they throw prisoners into them. You can't get out without a rope. And, if you had one, there's a Senegalese up above waiting to spit you if you show your head.

'But even if I had had a rope and a comrade to pull me out of the silo and deal with the Senegalese, I don't think I'd have tried anything. I was like someone who has done his best friend a damage when drunk and wants to die when he's sober again. At least, I didn't have to worry about that. I had attacked a superior officer on active service. I would be shot tomorrow. I had no regrets. I was even glad.

'The only thing about being glad in that sort of way is that you mustn't think too much if you want it to last. And I had all night. And what a night! It was freezing; stars clustered just above my hole and jackals howled quite close. Then I felt I didn't want to die.

'I thought of my father, who was still alive at that time. He was a good old chap, you know, a cobbler at Bizerta. He didn't really know what sort of blackguard his son had become. I had managed to conceal it from him. And now he was to hear that the Army had shot me.

'Morning took a long time coming, but it came all the same. I heard the company falling in by the silo. My eyes were burning. I was feverish. I thought of my old man. And yet, when they took me out of the hole, I put on a bold face. I believe I even pretended to smile.

'But, face to face with the lieutenant, I hadn't the courage to look at him.

'"I'd have had you shot like a dog," he said. "You deserve no better. But I've looked up your file. You've got an honest father. Because of him, you'll merely get this!"

'Before I had time to grasp what he meant, I felt one cheek burn like fire, then the other. He had cut my face open with his whip. Then... You know, I've never allowed anyone to lay a finger on me, neither on my face or elsewhere, but particularly my face. But that Christmas day I saluted, swallowed the blood that was running into my mouth and said: "Thank you, sir."'

For a long time past Hippolyte had not looked at me. He was staring at his hands.

When he had finished his story and raised his eyes, I realised that he had forgotten my presence. For his face immediately assumed an expression half-embarrassed, half-angry. Against me for having heard him out? Against himself for having stripped himself naked?

'Leave me alone,' he said.

His voice was low and dangerous. His hands, which till now had been lying flat on the table, suddenly contracted into hard masses of flesh and bone, like pieces of rock. He was controlling with difficulty a longing to wipe me out, to destroy me.

And yet Hippolyte was fond of me.

11
LOVE'S PENITENT

THE Pan-American Airways two-engined aircraft had left the plateau of Mexico City, which lies at an altitude of nearly 9,000 feet, at about noon. The day had been spent in the regular flight. We had made half a dozen landings in Mexican territory, on the outskirts of little towns, in the burning, fissured, dusty plain.

Thorn hedges, an oppressive heat that caught you by the throat and ill-dressed soldiers with slow gestures had received us on the short, yellow grass of the landing-fields.

On one of them, we had seen a rich *haciendero* hand his ten-year-old son over to a passenger he did not know till the next stop. At another, an Indian woman, feeding her child at the breast, had entered the plane.

At dusk, the Douglas landed on the Guatemala airfield, near the capital. I was to spend the night there and fly on next morning at dawn to Panama.

I knew no one in the country and, on landing, thought I would go to bed early and have a quiet night's sleep.

Things did not turn out that way.

I had left the Customs shed and was about to get into one of the company's buses conveying passengers from the airport to the town, which lay about thirty kilometres away, when I was almost run down by a fast-travelling car. It braked suddenly and stopped only a few feet from me.

'I thought the Douglas would gain a good quarter of an hour on the time-table with this wind behind it,' the man at the wheel cried in the most resonant French.

He jumped out and ran across to me.

'I nearly missed you,' he went on, 'and I could never have forgiven myself.'

Travelling inures you to surprise. The world tends to become reduced in size for a certain vagabond, adventurous clan. You get used to the most unexpected meetings.

It therefore seemed quite natural to meet in Central America a comrade I had known on various fronts in the 1914 war. I had not seen him again, after the Armistice, till one morning in 1930, when I had met him on the race-course in Addis Ababa then being used as an airfield by the Negus' aircraft. Since then our paths had diverged again and it was six years since we had heard of each other. And here was Lucas reappearing in Guatemala with his florid face, frank eyes, good humour and boyish manner.

We shook hands affectionately.

'Get into the car,' Lucas said. 'You'll arrive there quicker.'

He drove like a maniac, though a lucid one. The countryside fled past so quickly and night was falling so fast that I gave up all attempt to make anything out.

'There's not a bad view here from up above, with the volcanoes and their dark lakes in the centre,' Lucas said. 'But I must admit I've seen too much of it. I'm beginning to get blasé.'

He told me of the recent events of his life in a few curt, precise words, without suspecting the leaven of reverie they contained.

After Ethiopia, he had 'done' China as an instructor of volunteers. Then he had been an exhibition pilot in New Zealand. In San Francisco, he had drunk his savings. He had been in the pay of the Bolivian Government for a while. Now, he was chief adviser to the Guatemalan Air Force.

'I like it very much here,' Lucas concluded. 'Good pay. Good machines. The right kind of pupils. Hospitable, polite, amusing people who adore France.'

'What about the women?'

'Oh, I have simple tastes you know. I always manage all right. You'll see.'

Broad, clean streets between low houses with balconies, delightful gardens with trees and fountains, a feeling of space and harmony in the warm tropical night, these are the things I remember from that drive through the town. Lucas drove furiously; he was intoxicated by speed. But he had no need to deploy his skill as a driver that night. The districts through which we drove were completely deserted, and by the time we reached the hotel where Pan-American

Airways passengers usually put up, we had not passed more than three cars and a dozen pedestrians.

Having seen my room, which was large, with wide bay windows and dark furniture, and made a tour of the hall, the sitting-rooms and the patio to imbibe that vague, secret poetry peculiar to houses in hot countries, I joined Lucas in the bar.

'Tell me,' I asked him, 'why the hotel and the town are so deserted today.'

My friend looked at me suspiciously, as if he wanted to make sure I was not pulling his leg. But he realised I was serious and said: 'My dear chap, everyone's waiting for the procession. They're getting ready for it.'

'The procession? A local festival, I suppose?'

Lucas laughed so contagiously that I joined in though I had no idea what he was laughing at.

'You mustn't travel by air any more, my dear chap,' he said. 'It affects your head. It's not only a local festival, you know, several other countries have it too. Merely Good Friday.'

For a few seconds I was dumbfounded.

How had it happened that nothing during the previous days had reminded me that it was Easter Week? But Lucas's question: 'Where have you come from?' and my automatic reply: 'From Mexico!' gave me the explanation.

Mexico! All religious practices were forbidden there. In front of the cloisters of old monasteries, I had seen Indians indefinitely repeating on primitive stringed instruments the same shrill, plaintive note as if it were the only prayer they could offer up without another's help to a divinity whose essence they scarcely understood.

I told Lucas why I had forgotten. He nodded and said: 'I understand, I understand! In your place, it wouldn't have occurred to me either. But it's very different here, as you'll see later.'

We dined at the hotel. I tried to make Lucas talk as much as possible. I was eager to learn all I could about a country I would see only from the air and at night, like a dream. Lucas had been two years in Guatemala.

He had travelled all over it by air, on horseback and, wherever possible, by car. He had had engine failures which had landed him in almost inaccessible places. He had flown low over fantastic ruins in the jungle to get a better view of them. In short, he possessed a treasure from which I hoped to pick up a few crumbs.

But many men of action and the real professionals of adventure always think what they do and see to be perfectly natural and simple. Their trade, whether they be gold prospectors, barmen or pilots, interests them more than anything else.

For Lucas, the up-draughts from the craters, the damp air over the lagoons and the influence of the climate on engines were much more interesting than the Eden-like kindness of an Indian tribe with whom he had lived for nearly a month after making a forced landing, the wonderful embroideries he had brought back with him or the magic dances he had witnessed.

'I'm not a travel-book,' he ended by saying wearily. 'Let's go outside. I can at least promise you a spectacle.'

Out in the street, a distant, rhythmic rumour, and a redder glow than that created by the electric street-lamps made me hasten my pace. Soon, the ebbing and flowing sound became more distinct, a chanting broken by strange cries. I was almost running. Lucas stopped.

'Here's my house,' he said. 'Let's go in. I've got a balcony giving on to the main square.'

I had scarcely reached the balcony when a fascinating spectacle suddenly opened before me as if by magic. It was not surprising that till now the town had seemed deserted. All its inhabitants had gathered on a line of which the square beneath my eyes was the central point.

Soldiers with brilliant accoutrements were containing a fervent, ecstatic crowd gathered in massed ranks along the wide pavements. Between these two lines of people, who were intoxicated with the most naïve faith, the Good Friday procession was passing like some mystical phantasmagoria.

Standing on huge platforms, life-size wax figures represented the scenes of the Passion. Interior lighting made the bodies and faces of the statues translucent. The gold and the brocades shone in the light of the torches; and there were as many brilliant stones on the robes and accessories as there were stars in the sky. The huge images swayed on rafts above the crowd to the rhythm of the bearers' steps.

There were several dozen bearers to sustain the size and weight of each sacred platform. They wore black cloaks and black hoods. They chanted, while above them swayed, to a slow and gentle rhythm, the clear, luminous smiles and the anguish of the figures.

Further hooded penitents were gathered round about to take the place of the exhausted. Others again processed in closed ranks, interspersed here and there by groups of priests in sacerdotal robes carrying crucifixes, hosts and monstrances. Then another mystical raft would appear borne by more black penitents. Beneath the light of the torches, the extraordinary procession went slowly by, constantly renewed, always the same.

Due to the Indian faces of which the frieze of the crowd consisted almost exclusively, the tropical trees, the heavy, heady air, the expression of childish fanaticism shining in everyone's eyes and the Spanish tongue spoken in soft, native accents, I seemed to be watching a ceremony of the time of the conquistadors and viceroys, when the brutal adventurers of Castille, Navarre and Andalusia were creating new worlds.

By the time the last group of black penitents had broken up, it was nearly midnight.

'To belong to one of these cloaked fraternities, you have to be of good family and pay heavy dues,' Lucas said, shaking his head. 'Well, each to his own taste!'

The square was sad and empty.

'We can't go to bed immediately after that,' I said.

'Of course not,' Lucas replied. 'I'll take you to a place we call "the legation of love."'

I looked doubtful. Not from any particular puritanism, but because the places where women are sold inspire me with a certain dull melancholy and the opposite of desire.

'There's no choice,' Lucas said derisively. 'Everything's closed at this hour on such a day. Besides, you'll see, it's an agreeable place.'

It lay on the edge of the town, a fine low house which you entered through a sort of hall. It was delightfully cool with floor and walls of *azuléjos*. Beyond was an interior courtyard with arcades and fountains.

The main room had a varnished and nickel-plated bar, leather benches and polished wood tables. A guitarist was playing discreetly in a corner. A barman in a white jacket was manipulating a shaker.

There were three women: Gisèle, the manageress of the establishment, who was French; a good-looking Chilean girl; and a tall redhead from Los Angeles. They were young and had clear, fresh faces, showing none of the stigmata of unhealthy pallor and puffiness usually consequent on confinement.

They greeted Lucas with frank, simple pleasure and kissed him on the cheek.

'It's kind of you to come to visit us with your friend this evening,' the manageress said. 'We were very bored. It's certain no one else will come.'

Then, turning to me with all the eagerness of an expatriate, she said: 'Have you just come from France?'

'No, from Mexico and California,' I replied.

'What a pity,' Gisèle sighed.

Meanwhile Lucas had ordered drinks. While we were drinking each other's healths, a really marvellous creature came in. She had the grace and lightness of a bird at the moment it takes wing. Her limbs, the curves of her body, and the outline of her breasts and neck all had a grace that was at once supple and proud. Her face had a moving youthfulness and, by its smoothness of complexion, by the jet dark hair, the long, dark eyes and the expression of pride and native dignity, seemed to give her the appearance of being an effigy of a sacred virgin.

'Have a drink, Paquita,' Lucas said affectionately.

'I can't pronounce her real name,' Gisèle said. 'She's a young Indian. A real one. With no mixed blood. She comes from the high plateaux. Don't you think she's beautiful?'

Paquita came and sat beside me. She was neither forward nor shy, but as natural as a plant. I watched her hands resting on the table for a long time. I had never seen hands of so subtle and pure a shape.

We had been talking a long time when there was a sound of footsteps on the corridor tiles.

'At this time and today!' Gisèle murmured incredulously.

The door of the room opened and we all started or uttered a

cry of surprise. A black penitent in a hood stood on the threshold. His eyes moved from one face to another. He suddenly came across to Paquita. At first, she drew back in fear, but then her face expressed intense joy.

'Roman!' she cried. 'I'm sure you're Roman.'

The penitent threw back his hood and we saw that he was a very young man, with a shy, ardent face. He took Paquita's hand and murmured: 'Six months, for six whole months I haven't seen you, my flower.'

They went off into a corner together.

'What an adventure,' Lucas said. 'He's the son of one of the oldest families here. A year ago he came to have a drink at Gisèle's and the girl immediately cast a spell over him.'

'It's true, you know,' Gisèle said. 'He came back every night, but never touched her. His parents heard about it, took fright, and locked him up. He must have got permission to go out to join in the procession with his confraternity. Disguised by his hood, he's hurried round here.'

There was a great deal of discussion about it among the three women. I scarcely listened. I was hypnotised by the black penitent and the young Indian. They sat almost without speaking, just holding each other's hands and smiling like happy children.

'He comes of age next year and he'll marry her,' the Chilean prophesied.

'You're crazy,' Lucas replied. 'She can't even sign her name.'

'It won't be the first time such a thing has happened,' Gisèle wisely observed.

A few hours later, I left for Panama. I have not seen my friend Lucas since. And I do not know the end of the story.

12
THE MADMAN AT THE CARNIVAL

THE masks and banners of the Casablanca carnival made brilliant patches above the surface of the colourful, motley crowd. Arabs, Berbers, Jews, Maltese, Spaniards, merchants, letter-writers, water-carriers, money-changers, hillmen, sailors, important and less important nobles, children in rags, secret old men wrapped in majestic burnouses, all formed a moving, excited, tumultuous, rather childish background to the picturesque cavalcades and the flowered, allegorical floats that bore the dancers and singers from street to street.

From behind the veils concealing the faces of the Moslem women eyes like grains of jet in running water shone with a naïve delight in the marvellous.

The French population of the town was mostly gathered round the edges of the main square where the rejoicings were at their most frenzied. The bands on the stands and on the high cardboard floats played stridently. The sun was already hot and shone down on the disparate human crowd that was nevertheless fused into a whole by its primitive joy.

Suddenly, there was a wavering, a displacement of attention. All eyes turned from the procession and its tableaux to gaze up into the wide, pure sky from which came a regular throbbing that increased with every second.

'An aircraft,' the French said automatically.

'*Taïara*,' said the natives.

They were used to flying-machines and were already turning back to the procession, when the aircraft, as if pilotless, dived down towards the square. Voices and instruments suddenly fell silent. Then a strident clamour rose from the massed crowd.

The aircraft was on a level with the rooftops and was still diving. The propeller flashed brightly. It seemed about to destroy the crowd, cut it to pieces. The engine beat in one's ears like a tidal wave, a cyclone. It was the end of the world.

How small and narrow the square looked!

People pressed back into the side streets, became jammed against the walls, threw themselves to the ground. The performers jumped from the floats. The musicians dropped their instruments. But, almost at the last moment, the aircraft, which seemed out of control, came out of its dive, almost brushed the walls and flew out of the well into which it had plunged.

The panic-stricken crowd had not yet grasped what had happened before the aircraft was on them a second time.

'He's mad!' some shouted of the pilot.

The Moslems were invoking the Divine mercy. Screaming women pulled their veils over their eyes so as not to look on death. Once again, the aircraft flew past the roofs, the walls and the heads, and the square was empty.

While the excitement was spreading through Casablanca and the event, in distorted and exaggerated form, was the subject of conversation in the most distant bazaars and the smallest booths, the aircraft which had disrupted the carnival was landing gently on the airfield of the Compagnie Latécoère which, at that time, carried the mail between Toulouse and Dakar. A young man got out. He had very blue eyes, very pink cheeks and a most innocent expression.

'I saw the procession from quite close at hand. What a corrida!' he said in the most nonchalant way to the native workmen whose brown hands were pushing his machine into the hangar.

Marcel Reine was twenty-four. It was his day on duty at the airfield and he had not been able to resist the temptation to have a little fun too on this day of general rejoicing.

He had meant no harm. It was just a joke and seemed to him no more serious than the 'country-house forced landings' for which he had become famous during his military service. He would invent an engine failure, land in a field or a clearing near some fine house, be lavishly entertained and smile at the girls with his white young teeth.

Once again, Reine was right. He was not sacked by the Compagnie Latécoère and he remained popular in Casablanca.

This colourful and rather childish episode was a perfect example of an exceptional pilot's temperament, of the climate of a profession that was still in its youth and of the place and time at which the event took place. It has been inconceivable for a long time past. The mere shape and size of commercial aircraft were shortly to make it impossible. Indeed, can one imagine an airline pilot with his uniform, his scientific training and his quasi-official attitude capable of such an escapade? What sanctions would follow upon it!

But at that time extreme youth, love of fun, heedless courage and a certain indulgence coalesced to make things like this possible. The period of the disrupted carnival belonged to the palmy days of the Casablanca–Dakar line and its pilots. Marcel Reine and his comrades had the splendid luck of being the same age as that of an enterprise that was built on risk, sacrifice and poetry.

This was in 1926. Flying was no more than twenty years old. There was no need to be very old to have known its first pioneers. Blériot, Farman and Morane were still working.

The legendary aces who had survived the 1914 war were under thirty. There was still something almost fabulous about the profession of the air. The idea of taking an aircraft merely to get more quickly from one place to another still seemed ridiculous and mad to most people.

From this timorous respect for the air the pilots drew much prestige.

In the military formations and the civilian companies, which resembled them, there was often a reflection of that freedom the conquerors of a new element had known. Provided the pilot had a faultless hand and eye and carried out his duties scrupulously, both general opinion and his superiors were prepared to forgive him much. The conditions of flying and the precariousness of their machines maintained these men in a sort of heroic confederation. To excel in it, certain singularities of temperament were required. This was understood; and it was admitted that such natures should not be subjected to too narrow a discipline.

No doubt Marcel Reine would have joined the air force and then commercial flying even if they had not conferred these privileges which, as much as the risk and the fascination of the air, attracted young men about the year 1920. His skill, his audacity, his love of speed, and his profound need to work in a new, clean domain, all marked him out for the profession of long-distance pilot.

On the other hand, no one was better suited to enjoy his share of those freedoms which, together with the daily difficulties and mortal perils, were part of a pilot's life. Reine came from Paris, indeed was an out and out Parisian. You saw it at a glance. All the courage, intrepidity, modesty, kindness and wit the wonderful city had accumulated in its population through the centuries had been transmitted to Marcel Reine. He was stamped by it. From the district of the Halles, where his parents had a large business, he derived frank and downright speech, a gift for repartee and a taste for good living, but also common sense and a capacity for honest work. For, in spite of the many happy pranks which made Reine famous from Toulouse to the Cordillera of the Andes, he always retained his balance, a certain bourgeois solidity, a practical view both of people and things, and a complete adherence to the virtues and honour of his profession.

And all this was founded on a superb physical vitality, which was apparent in his magnificently candid and intrepid expression, the bursting health of his cheeks, the brightness of his eyes and the brave, frank gaiety of his smile.

Such was Marcel Reine when he scattered the procession and the crowd at the carnival.

I never met anyone who was insensible to Reine's charm. And I imagine that Didier Daurat, the managing director of the Compagnie Latécoère, could not entirely escape its influence.

Nevertheless, sentimental influences had little hold on Daurat. A former squadron leader in the air force, he commanded the pilots of the airline as he had led other young men in time of war, that is to say with a firmness which amounted to inflexible strictness. Yet, by some secret privilege which appertains only to true leaders, this strictness, far from arousing the indignation or from discouraging the men under him, drew all that was finest and best out of them. Daurat knew well how to choose his men, lead them, punish them and give them a sense of their own greatness.

If Reine had delayed the mail only once by his own fault, failed to go to the help of a comrade, or turned back in a sandstorm, Daurat would not have forgiven him the carnival scandal. He would have been sacked that night. But, when Daurat heard of the crazy behaviour of the aircraft over the festival square, he must have thought of that aircraft's pilot, with his boyish face, braving for months on end the storms and rains of the Spanish coast, defying the African desert, ignoring fatigue and fear, flying always and everywhere with a high heart, with joy and luck, as he risked his young life for the mail and the line.

Reine had never had cold feet, had never hesitated or turned back. And he was a marvellous pilot. Daurat kept Reine. There were not many men born capable of coping with the demands made on them, by the incredible task set them above the mountains, the seas and the sand. Reine ranked as one of the best of these men. Daurat's reasoned indulgence was witness to it.

To grasp with any precision the qualities of the men who at that time kept the Casablanca–Dakar line going, one must go back to its beginnings.

After the terrible years of the 1914–18 war, there had been a period of inglorious relaxation in France. The country devoted itself to a scramble for money, a thirst for pleasure or merely to a desire for cheap and easy tranquillity. This climate, symptomatic of a widespread renegation, did not suit the boys emerging into manhood, who had the zest, ambitions and faith worthy of their age and their country. There was a virgin field, defined, healthy, glamorous and dangerous, open to them. They instinctively chose flying.

The only means of access to it was through the army. There they served their apprenticeships and then sought to put the techniques they had acquired to good use by becoming pilots in civil airlines. This was what Mermoz, Saint-Exupéry and Guillaumet did. This was what Reine did.

How did these young men of the same age, but of very different origins and education, find themselves under the command of Didier Daurat and on the long run that was one day to extend as far as the Pacific? Why were none of them on the Paris–London, Paris–Berlin or Bucharest runs? There are problems of predestination, chance, unconscious choice and individual fate which are impossible to resolve. It would indeed be useless to attempt to do so. Human enterprise requires these coincidences to attain to the epic level. That, surely, is enough. And it is enough to remember the conditions in which the air mail from Casablanca to Dakar was developed to realise how the pilots forged their line and how the line forged its pilots.

In 1918, before the end of the war, an aircraft manufacturer, Pierre Latécoère, with foresight amounting to genius, realised the possibilities of civil aviation. There were no commercial aircraft. Reconnaissance machines and bombers (which alone could be used as transports) had a speed of seventy-five to one hundred miles an hour. They could remain in the air for four or five hours at most. Their single engines afforded no safety. They had no wireless. But it was with these machines, which today seem prehistoric, that Latécoère founded the first airline. He asserted that one day it would link France with Chile. Didier Daurat and his pilots gave life and form to this dream. The mail was first carried regularly from Toulouse to Casablanca in Bréguet 15s, of which the model dated from 1917.

In uncertain aircraft, of which the engines had been patched up again and again, protected only by a small windscreen, with no other instruments for navigation but a primitive compass, the pilots flew through storm, fog and narrow defiles, surmounting the dangers and the lack of equipment by their courage, their experience and their instinct.

Having achieved the conquest of the Spanish sky, they set about the run from Casablanca to Dakar.

In the same aircraft, which were now several years older, they confronted the sun, the simoun, the desert and the wild Moors.

In 1250 miles their only chances of refuelling or refuge were three little white patches, three strongpoints surrounded by barbed wire. These were Cap Juby, Villa Cisneros and Port-Étienne.

An engine failure—and they were chronic—forced them to land between these desert redoubts and presented a choice of capture by the wild tribes or death by thirst.

The picture presented by the brilliance of the sea, the hardness of the sky, the sand stretching away to infinity, nomads in blue veils moving from place to place in response to some mysterious urge and, above all these wild, secret and mortal dangers, a man, unarmed, vulnerable, alone, moving through the air suspended in a tiny, fragile cell, has a quality of fable and of myth.

But, for Reine and his comrades, there was nothing supernatural or even extraordinary about their task. They were tough and realistic young men. They merely loved life and their profession. They lived poetry without realising it.

Among these admirable and unsophisticated young men, there were no doubt two who had a clear idea and an almost mystic sense of what they were doing: Mermoz and Saint-Exupéry. But they were so completely at one with their companions, were so much just 'Saint-Ex,' and 'Le Grand Jean,' that their behaviour was no different from that of the other pilots. The constellation, with its stars, their place and their greatness, had not yet become established in the sky.

Casablanca was the principal home port for the pilots of the line. They formed a clan within which each lived as he liked and in accordance with his temperament. But they met several times a day on the airfield, in the Company's offices or in public places.

Émile Lécrivain, Marcel Reine, Guillaumet, Riguelle, Emler, Gourp, Érable, Jean Mermoz, Étienne, Guerrero, Depelker and Ham all died on the job.

How young they were then, how cheerful and how gay! And the line had the peculiar charm of all beginnings. Without knowing it, its pilots, flight by flight, were indubitably accomplishing the most noble and daring work undertaken between the two wars. It did not weigh on their strong shoulders. Health, gaiety, work and comradeship wonderfully filled their lives. They spoke of their flights, their accidents, their encounters with storms and Moors as simply as do workers in a peaceful and sedentary trade. From time to time a brief silence would interrupt their gay talk. Someone, by a fatal association of thought, had reminded them of the name of a dead comrade.

As in every human group, deeper affinities linked certain pilots in special friendship; this applied to Mermoz and Étienne, and to Guillaumet and Saint-Exupéry.

But, if one had to name one of them who was beloved by them all, I do not think it is going too far to say that Reine headed the list. He owed this privilege to the fact that never a word or an action gave the lie to the qualities evident in his face. His joy in life and his kindness were irresistible. He could cheer the most careworn with his happy gusto and his comic rages. His language had a surprising savour. No one was more generous than he. He was a stranger to boredom, envy and vanity. He was a madcap with a heart of gold.

When you saw him—short, sturdy, resolute, fair-haired, blue-eyed and pink of cheek—you felt closer to childhood and its games. Reine's pranks had become a legend. There was the story of the carnival, and that of the cab-horse he unharnessed outside a night-club, led up to the bar and, with the utmost composure, proceeded to make drunk. There were his numerous and complicated love affairs, whose unexpected quarrels and reconciliations formed an extravagant pattern. There were engine-repairs made in heroic circumstances, the rescue of Larre-Borjes, the Uruguayan airman, under Moorish bullets, and the two brief but harsh captivities he had himself suffered at the hands of the natives.

Reine's popularity was not only among his comrades, pilots, managers of airfields, mechanics and labourers throughout the line. He was forgiven all his excesses both in Casablanca and Dakar. Elfin bells, at once festive and poetic, seemed always to be ringing wherever he went. He entered, smiled and won all hearts.

And so, sometimes the winged courier of the desert, sometimes the indefatigable and darling *enfant terrible* of Casablanca, Reine spent three violent, heedless and perfectly happy years till the day of his great ordeal.

Édouard Serre, a former student of the École Polytechnique and a pilot during the war, was on the managerial staff of Aéropostale. This was the name the Compagnie Latécoère had taken in 1928 when it was absorbed by Marcel Bouilloux-Laffont's finance group. The line had taken a great stride forward and there were significant developments. New aircraft, beacons on the airfields, a radio network were all being hurriedly installed at Toulouse, in Spain, in Africa and in South America, where Mermoz was already performing his miracles.

Serre, who was making a tour of inspection of the airfields, took Reine's aircraft to go from Casablanca to Dakar. There was nothing premeditated about their flying together. On that summer's day, Reine was in charge of the mail. Serre went with him. He intended going on to Brazil. Shared misfortune associated these two men, who would normally have separated a few hours after meeting, for the rest of their lives.

As they were flying over the Spanish enclave of Rio de Oro, where the most dangerous Moorish tribes lived subject to no control, Marcel Reine was blinded by night and mist. There were no blind-flying instruments in those days. You had to rely on chance and instinct. Chance was at once both with and against Reine. He believed he was over the sea when in fact drift had taken him over the desert.

Sandy hills and rocky plateaux rose to a height of a thousand feet. Reine was flying at precisely this altitude. With his engine running full out he hit the very summit of an invisible hill.

If the aircraft had been flying three feet lower, nothing could have prevented a total crash. But his line of flight allowed Reine, though flying blind, to react instinctively to the controls and he succeeded in landing safely though the machine was badly damaged.

A few hours after sunrise, Reine and Serre were captured by R'Guibat warriors.

An adventure then began which was to last four months and take the men subjected to it back into an age of barbarism.

One can imagine no more diverse characters than those of these companions in misfortune. Serre had very dark hair, was very thin and very frail. His big brown kindly eyes shone behind his spectacles with a profound interior fire. A passionate intellectual, he lived only for abstractions. Absent-minded, naïve, generous, in spite of all his science and culture, he was less sophisticated than Reine, who often treated him as a sort of childish visionary. But, different though they were, they had great courage and genuineness in common. And this enabled them to bear their appalling captivity with a similar stoicism.

Reine and Serre gave a detailed account of their captivity in a book that appeared some time after their liberation. The book is good-humoured and serenely philosophical; it might be relating an episode in *The Thousand and One Nights*. It tells of a brutal master and a wife in love with his prisoner; of moving from camp to camp: of the life of the tents: the pastures, scented tea, caravans moving across the sandy hills.... Singular pride and modesty forbid the least complaint.

In fact, it was a desperately hard servitude. Fed on filthy scraps, perpetually tormented by a thirst they could not assuage with the stagnant water that was doled out to them drop by drop, burnt by a pitiless sun, lacking clothes and linen, their feet bare and bleeding, their hands torn, Reine and Serre were subjected for many weeks to the most arduous labour. They served as beasts of burden. With their nails they tore from the arid earth the meagre twigs for the evening camp-fire.

Since their masters belonged to different sections of the tribe, they were separated; and this they felt more keenly than all their physical sufferings. When they chanced to meet in a joint camp, they did not at first recognise each other. Each was grieved by his friend's appearance.

The price of their ransom was agreed only after months of bargaining. Two skeletons were handed over to Fort Juby. They were covered with a sort of dark, scaly parchment which was their skin. Vermin swarmed in their open sores.

Nevertheless, when Marcel Reine landed at Casablanca, where he was awaited by seventeen young women who were in love with him, he was fit enough to go through the exhausting welcome the town extended to its favourite. His physical and moral resilience were such, and his faculty of recovery so great, that a few days on board a little coaster had sufficed to restore his strength and equilibrium.

Five years later, Casablanca was still talking of the resurrection of Marcel Reine.

It continued in Paris, to which he was sent on leave. His pleasure was spoilt only by the ceremonies organised in his honour. They made him really unhappy. The formality and the speeches embarrassed him as unseemly. He could not understand why he should be the object of them. Instead of being flattered, he felt like an unjustly punished child.

But how he made up for these ceremonies when they were over! No one knew better than Marcel Reine how to amuse himself and no one was more gladly entertained.

I first met him at the end of this period, as he was about to go back to the airline. Even after all these years, I remember very clearly the surprise and incredulity I felt on first seeing him. Though he was twenty-seven, he still looked almost a child. The bloom on his skin, the expression in his eyes, the movements of his face and body were none of them slowed, faded or impaired. He resembled those very young sailors who seem endued with the reflection, the freshness of sky and sea.

Marcel Reine's speech and manner disconcerted me still further. They were those of a charming and lively young Parisian, speaking a wonderful slang, pointed and gay, who might never have left his city. You could not imagine him flying over sea and sand, through storms, moonless nights and the simoun. You could not place him in his flying-machine in the immensity of the sky. You could not believe in his terrible adventure and that, only two months ago, he had been following the caravans of the blue Moors, a slave with bleeding feet.

Shortly after Reine left Paris, the management of Aéropostale authorised me—passengers were not yet accepted on the African line—to fly from Casablanca to Dakar. I travelled with Serre who was continuing the inspection that had been interrupted by his capture.

Between Cape Juby and Villa Cisneros, we ran into a sandstorm as thick as mud. The aircraft shuddered under the violent gusts. The ends of the wings were lost in a yellow, sulphurous, viscous cloud that seemed to fill the universe. Blind flying was as yet unknown. We got lost over the sea, turned back towards the coast, and very nearly ran into the cliffs that appeared suddenly out of the gloom. In two years of flying in the war I had never been so frightened. But Émile Lécrivain, piloting with a sure and sensitive hand, saved us.

Like Reine, he was a Parisian of ancient origin. He came from Belleville. Lécrivain's gaiety and gusto were more sensitive, more nervous than his comrade's. He played the violin, sang and danced superbly. I had spent an evening in Casablanca with him and his friends at which he had been the centre of gaiety. But as soon as he was at the controls, his expression changed. It became serious and concentrated. Throughout the sandstorm and until we landed it had a fierce and magnificent austerity.

After the first moments of animal joy at being safe, we learned with anxiety that the aircraft coming from Dakar was two hours late. The simoun was still raising its floating, moving wall of sticky particles. We waited on the airfield. Time ceased to have its ordinary duration. At last, we heard an aircraft, invisible in the curtain of sand suspended between earth and sky, circling above our heads. It suddenly emerged from its yellow prison and landed a few paces away. Reine jumped out of the pilot's seat.

I really thought I was seeing a different man from the one I knew. There was nothing in common between the heedless, mobile face I remembered so well and this serious, fixed, drawn, hollow, ochre mask, the same mask I had seen Lécrivain wear.

The elements of the storm had lent part of their secret and their power to Reine's features, not only in the thick dust that covered them, but in the human force and energy that had held the sandstorm in check and at bay.

Reine's high, unconscious tension lasted only an instant. He suddenly burst out in comical cursing of the weather, the sky, the line and life in general. Then, as he laughed at his own anger, he resembled nothing so much as a dirty little boy.

Reine and Serre were meeting once again in the Rio de Oro, the scene of their captivity. Beyond the barbed wire, they had suffered intolerable experiences together. But, while Serre was trying with evident emotion to reconstruct the climate of their adventure, entering the tents of the nomad traders who were camping at Villa Cisneros that day, conversing with them in Arabic, and drinking the sweet mint tea he had prepared so often without being allowed to wet his thirst-cracked lips in it, Reine went to the canteen and ordered several bottles of beer.

No more than in Paris was I able to get a word out of him about his profession or his captivity. But I had seen him get out of the aircraft and I understood him better. Reine's strength and admirable integrity were based on his innate refusal to think of the object of the action apart from the action itself, and the unconscious determination not to allow his profound reserves of instinct to be impaired.

He was supposed to hand over his aircraft to Lécrivain and fly us to Dakar. But Lécrivain also wanted to go on to Dakar. They argued like schoolboys. Right was on Reine's side. Lécrivain was appealing and tenacious. In the end, they decided to play for it. And these two men, who had just fought one of the hardest battles of the air, played dice for who should continue the journey.

I had a feeling that Reine managed to lose out of sheer kindness of heart.

This was the last mail Reine was to fly on the Casablanca–Dakar line. Since his liberation, he had been appointed to South America. But Daurat had wanted the Moors' captive to fly once more over the regions in which he had been held a slave. Daurat knew that Reine's former masters would hear of it at once by the mysterious desert telegraph which had its source in the Spanish forts. And he thought this was good both for the pilot's dignity and the prestige of the line.

Reine therefore left the shores of Morocco, Mauritania and Senegal for the coasts of Brazil, Uruguay and the Argentine. Instead of the simoun, he had to deal with pamperos and cyclones. Instead of the infinite sands, he flew over virgin jungle. Mermoz, Guillaumet and Saint-Exupéry were his companions once more.

For years he indulged simultaneously in epic duties and unbridled pleasures. The parties at night in his house in Rio Janeiro sometimes became so boisterous that the neighbours fired revolver shots at his windows to obtain a little quiet.

But when I met Reine again in Buenos Aires, he had got over his bacchanal period and had married. He lived in a quiet and restful villa in the suburbs. His wife was a simple and charming hostess. Two dogs wandered about the cool rooms.

Few people visited him apart from other pilots, Pourchas, his wireless-operator, and two or three friends resident in the Argentine, among them the bohemian painter Laverdet to whom Reine was inexhaustibly generous.

The quiet happiness of his home was reflected in Reine's face. He had settled down, filled out and grown calmer. You were more aware of the common sense and practical philosophy that had, indeed, always been there but which his vitality and exuberance had hitherto tended to mask. Yet, he had grown no older. His colouring, expression and, above all, his heart were still the same. He had not betrayed his youth. He had merely allowed age to qualify it. It remained intact with all its liveliness and vitality.

I was in South America to obtain any information I could about the life and flying exploits of the great Mermoz, who had recently crashed in the Atlantic. How well Reine talked of Mermoz! With what simple, loyal, inimitable friendship! And I remembered that Mermoz, in a fit of disgust in Paris, had once cried: 'Thank God for the airline, and thank God Guillaumet and Reine are with it!'

Guillaumet, indeed, had succeeded Mermoz on the regular crossing of the Cordillera de los Andes after Mermoz had conquered and mastered the mountains that had previously been impassable. When Mermoz asked Guillaumet to fly the Atlantic with him, Reine had succeeded Guillaumet. There was a certain splendour about this succession to an aerial heritage.

The three men used the same machine, a Potez 25, which had no radio, no blind-flying instruments, no covered cockpit and no oxygen. The pilot's safety was dependent on a single engine. In this machine he had to brave the frosts of very high altitudes, blinding fogs, terrible winds and snowstorms amid peaks and valleys of gleaming, tragic desolation.

This period was over when I went from the Argentine to Chile. The three-engined Air France machine was enclosed, heated and had perfected instruments. The permanent crew consisted of a barman, a second pilot-mechanic, a radio-operator and a chief pilot, who was Reine.

Neither his position nor his responsibilities frightened him, but he had a childish and touching dislike of their outward forms. He obstinately refused to wear a civil pilot's uniform. The most he could be persuaded to do was to don a blue mackintosh and the regulation cap. But he wore them only when leading his crew out to board the aircraft. Once on board, he immediately discarded them. This was the first thing he did at the outset of our flight.

I was lucky enough to be the only passenger and to have exceptionally fine weather. I was thus able to enjoy both a sublime spectacle and Reine's hospitality without hindrance—for, indeed, did not the wild Andes with their peaks, precipices and eternal snows, their condors quartering the pitiless sky and their bounding guanacos belong to him? Was this not the inheritance bequeathed him by Mermoz and Guillaumet?

Reine named the highest peaks, which run up to over 22,000 feet. He pointed out the Christ of the Cordillera. He showed me the plateau on which Mermoz had struggled for three days to repair his damaged machine before setting off on a fabulous course that ran from ledge to ledge, and the little lake from which Guillaumet had set out on the superhuman task, in which he succeeded, of conquering the Cordillera de los Andes on foot.

He gave me cognac to drink and asserted that the altitude improved its taste. And he said with conviction: 'You're a lucky bastard. I've never seen such fine weather.'

Thinking of his charming house, of the years he had spent in constant danger, and of the comfort in which he could live even if he gave up flying, I asked him if he did not sometimes think of the possibility of a fatal accident. He looked severely at me, as if I had committed a solecism.

'That's not a question one asks,' he muttered and continued to play the part of a hospitable landlord. In similar mood he showed me Santiago de Chile and its neighbourhood, the peach-trees in blossom, the streets and squares, the nightclubs in the town, and the next morning took me to Valparaiso by car. He continued to play the host.

Out of regard for the truth, I must say that he in no sense limited himself to the part of host and guide. He enjoyed his fair share of our dissipations. For a few hours, I knew once again the wild companion, who was so indefatigable in pleasure, of the nights of Casablanca and Montmartre.

On our way back, I said: 'Santiago means permission to relax then?'

'Things are as they are,' he replied, with all the embarrassment of a child caught at fault. 'The Baronne' (this was what he always called his wife), 'doesn't know about it.'

There was a gleam of the old humour, of the love of a joke, in his bright eyes.

'Of course, it wasn't so easy at first,' he said. 'The Baronne suspected something. I always came home absolutely out. I accounted for it by the fatigue of the flight and the altitude. But she wasn't having any. The Baronne refused to believe me. So I had an idea.'

We were flying back over the Christ of the Andes. Reine gave him a friendly wave and went on: 'I took the Baronne on a flight. Like today, there were no other passengers. I didn't turn on the oxygen. And on various pretexts I made the Baronne hump our suitcases. It took her two days to recover. Ever since, she's been all over me when I get home.'

And his fresh, ingenuous, irresistible laugh—the laugh of the old days—rang out in the cockpit.

Reine owned a *fazenda* about a hundred kilometres north of Rio de Janeiro. He was fond of this property, which he had bought cheaply, and would sometimes say with evident affection: 'It's a pretty little place. I shall retire there.'

The pretty little place was a huge estate in keeping with the outsize proportions of Brazil. I doubt if he had ever made a complete tour of the hills and valleys he owned. Mermoz had ridden for hours across the *fazenda* without ever reaching its boundaries.

Half-caste Indians lazily cultivated a few parcels of land. Half-wild horses roamed over it. Monkeys swarmed in the tropical undergrowth. The streams, which the torrential rains turned into rivers, flowed between the coffee-trees, the mangoes, and the banana-trees to which no one attended.

On the edge of his paradise, on fallow land, had been built two little rustic but comfortable houses. It was here that Reine, when he flew the airmail on the Brazil line, had spent happy, idle days with his comrades. It was here, so he said, that he intended soon to lead a quiet life, when he had retired from being a pilot.

Was he serious? Doubtless he no longer had that impetuous enthusiasm which had driven him on in the days when both he and the line were in their first youth. Hierarchy, routine and red tape at the top had replaced Didier Daurat's passionate and lucid audacity. Reine had much preferred the manoeuvrability, the uncertainties and the heroic solitude of the cockpit of the Bréguet 15s, the Laté 26s and the Potez 25s to the new, safe machines with their size, weight and load of passengers. He felt diminished by their very mass and appearance. And now they were even trying to put him into uniform!

There were other deeper, more important reasons for his occasional fits of depression. At the hands of the financiers and administrators in Paris, the network the line had covered, and at the cost of so many lives, had been curtailed. France was abandoning the splendid conquest for which the bravest and most disinterested of her sons had risked everything. The Americans and the Germans were supplanting them.

Mermoz had died because of this dereliction. And now that he was dead, there was no one of sufficient stature to fight it. When Reine felt his powerlessness too deeply, he consoled himself with the thought of his *fazenda*.

But he was appointed to the trans-Atlantic line. He accepted without hesitation. He flew between Dakar and Natal (Brazil) till France collapsed before the advance of the German tanks. Flying the Atlantic was then forbidden the French. A few months later Reine was appointed to the Marseilles–Beirut line.

One day in November 1940, I met him on the terrace of a Marseilles café. We had not seen each other for about eighteen months; since before the war, in another age and another world.

We did not discuss the disastrous times. There was always something about Reine that forbade useless words when deep emotions were involved.

His eyes and complexion still retained their unalterable youthfulness. But he had almost lost his smile. And when he told me he was going to see his parents though, as usual, he referred to them in his slang as '*mes vieux*' and '*le frangin*,' he no longer said '*Paname*' for occupied Paris, but merely 'up there.'

A few days after Marcel Reine returned to Marseilles from Paris, an aircraft was due to fly to Beirut with the mail. It was Guillaumet's not Reine's turn to pilot it. Nevertheless, Reine wanted to go with him.

Why? Was it boredom or the depression due to occupied Paris? Was it a need to find in flight the old happy elixir of escaping into the sky?

They set off together. Guillaumet who, according to his own account to Saint-Exupéry, had done what no beast could do in the Andes, and Reine whose laughter had consoled Mermoz.

Why and how did their peaceful, unarmed aircraft get mixed up in one of the naval air battles which were then frequently taking place in the Mediterranean? It will always remain a mystery. Their aircraft was shot down in flames, a total loss.

On the charts sailors use along the Moroccan and Mauritanian coasts you may read beside the names of Mermoz, Lécrivain, Guillaumet and Saint-Exupéry, each designating a cape or a bay, that of Marcel Reine. Soon, no one will know that this name was that of a brave, charming Parisian, who had blue eyes and rosy cheeks.

13
THE BANQUET

NIGHT had long fallen on 24 December 1942, when the wretched little train, making its last shuttle journey between Perpignan and Port Vendres, stopped at Collioure. The travellers got out of the dark carriages, tramped through the mud and the night to the exit gate, which was indicated only by the dim red glow of a veiled light, and quickly dispersed through the unlit streets of the village.

Rain, cold as sleet, whipped their faces. Everyone was hurrying home to warmth and family, some with a little butter, bacon or chicken, some with a handful of eggs, flour or sugar, some with a pot of jam or honey. All these provisions had been obtained after long search, difficult bargaining, and at the cost of considerable risk. In these famished times, they assumed a peculiar value on Christmas Eve.

However, these people had come to the end of their travels and were arriving home. For me the journey—and what a journey!—was just beginning.

I waited, according to my instructions, till the little, cold, dark train moved on, till the porter had gone into the station building which was blacked-out all round, and then made my way to the left of the station as the guide had instructed me at Perpignan the day before. I was aware that shadowy figures were following me. My suitcase, though small and light, seemed suddenly terribly heavy. Militia? Police? Gestapo?

But I quickly recognised those small, furtive movements which seem, as it were, reduced to the bodily extremities. The shadowy figures were as anxious as I was. I was disgusted with myself for being frightened already, when there were so many customs men, police, secret agents and trained dogs—French, German and Spanish—to confront; as well as the dark tracks, the doubtful refugees, and many other possible dangers, such as traps and ambushes, to surmount before the end of this secret journey to England, and the Free France of General de Gaulle.

Our guide suddenly appeared from nowhere. He was short, nervous and spoke French with a strong Catalan accent.

'Hurry up, hurry up,' he whispered impatiently. 'Hurry up! You've already been here too long. Follow me quickly, one by one. Keep well apart. Hurry . . .'

There were six of us fugitives and our file spread out behind the little man in the night and the rain. Nevertheless, there were two figures in the file, of very different heights and shapes, who stayed close to each other. I admit I paid very little attention to them.

When we had left Collioure, the file of fugitives drew together. It was very necessary; in the dark, we had only the back of the man in front to guide us. It was thus we reached the first line of wooded hills that were the foothills of the Pyrenees. Rain dripped from the branches and trunks on to the sticky ground.

Suddenly, the whole group came instinctively to a halt. A man had emerged from the confused ranks of the trees. He was tall and strong and looked gigantic in the dark under the trees. On his back he was carrying an enormous package; its volume gave his silhouette a huge, humped outline. Fear—ignoble, absurd but invincible—assailed me once again. And once again needlessly.

'This is my companion, Juan,' the guide said. 'He will walk in front. He's taller and we shall be able to see him better. And I'll come behind to make sure everyone keeps up. From now on, we must move quickly, very quickly, and without stopping.'

José, the guide, switched on an electric torch and directed it at each of us in turn. He saw my suitcase. The torch wavered, he swore in Spanish and said: 'You'll never be able to make the mountains with that in your hand!'

Big Juan came over without a word, unrolled a sack from about his waist, put my suitcase in the sack, tore the sack down to the middle and knotted the two ends round my neck. He laughed softly and said: 'The smuggler's method.'

Meanwhile, José continued his inspection.

'Those shoes,' he said to one of the shadowy figures of the group. 'Those shoes! How do you think you're going to cross the mountains in them?'

'Forgive me, I was unable to get any others, but, I assure you, I shan't delay you,' a timid, submissive voice replied.

All the fugitives except one turned at the sound of the voice. The dark and the similarity of the mackintoshes we wore had prevented our realising till now that we had a woman among us. I remembered the short figure which, in spite of the guide's injunctions, had remained close to a large, taller figure in the file.

'Let's get going. Hurry!' José said nervously.

From then on, physical tension, muscular effort, an elementary struggle against the ruggedness of the ground and the rising tide of fatigue became the elements of life itself. The world had shrunk to a few yards of dark and dangerous earth. The horizon was reduced to a few ill-defined tree-trunks. And there were the traps set by invisible branches, bogs, loose stones and rocks as dark as the night and as slippery as the rain. And through this sort of ambush, this continuous snare, one had to go on hoisting one's body and one's clothes, grown heavy in the soaking icy rain, ever higher.

My suitcase, which I could certainly not have carried in my hand, was sawing into the small of my back; the ends of the sack, knotted round my neck, were strangling me. I kept on wondering confusedly by what miracle a man who was not used to it could climb like this without spraining his ankles and collapsing from sheer exhaustion. But a loose stone or a particularly rough patch of ground would prevent all connected thought, and I became no more than a panting animal, bathed in sweat despite the cold, a blind animal concerned solely to place his feet in the tracks of the animal who tottered, blind, breathless as he was, in front of him.

From time to time, I thought of the young woman and, wherever the nature of the ground allowed it, I looked at her. She was pressed against one of the fugitives, as if tied to him. Then, I would forget everything in the world, except the path, or the mud, or the rock immediately under my feet, or the beating of my heart which seemed to grow ever quicker and more violent, and to be rising into my throat as if to strangle me.

Suddenly, and I can remember, even after all these years, the sense of deliverance and of happiness spreading through my body, there was a halt. I thought we had covered the first stage of our journey. But José, coming from the back of the file, passed me swearing. A moment later, he asked the young woman: 'What's the matter? Your high heels?'

'No,' she said. And, after a moment's hesitation, she added with tenderness and infinite pity: 'He's had a bad knee ever since the Spanish Civil War.'

We had all drawn nearer to the couple. It was the big, tall, heavy man who was leaning on the woman's arm. José swore at length.

'And you didn't tell me!' he muttered between his teeth.

He turned to me, who knew him better than the others, and grumbled: 'I told you it was more profitable to smuggle saccharine or even radio sets, as my friend Juan does, than to take people across.'

'Don't worry, we'll follow on,' the woman said.

She placed her shoulder under her companion's armpit and, serving him as a crutch, began leading him up the hill. José swore quietly. 'Follow Juan,' he said to us. 'I'll join you later with these two.'

We had no difficulty in passing the entwined couple, and big Juan, his enormous package on his back, led us on into the mountains and the night. He moved with a light, infernally rapid pace. And it went on and on . . .

At last we came to the clearing where our march was due to end. It was still raining. The ground was a bog. But this did not prevent our collapsing full length into the sticky mud without even removing our loads.

Only big Juan put his radio set down carefully. Then he began dragging branches of dead wood towards the clearing. He piled them high, unearthed a petrol tin and poured some over the wood. We were just beginning to recover our breath when the bonfire burst into flame.

José appeared. Behind him came the young woman and the man she was supporting with her whole body held rigid.

He had a very handsome face, fine-drawn and intense; it was made even more handsome by suffering and by the light of the bonfire which emphasised the features. There was nothing remarkable about his companion's face under the scarf that covered her hair, except an extraordinary, an almost childish expression of mingled sweetness and stubbornness.

She removed a rucksack from the man's shoulders and helped him to sit on it, with one leg outstretched. Then she made him take off his coat, jacket and shirt and put them to dry at the fire. Only then did she sit down herself and take some food from a haversack she was wearing.

José threw some wood onto the huge fire and said, 'You couldn't want better weather to cross the frontier. In this rain and mist you could set the forest alight and no one would see you.'

He laughed nervously and added, 'It's a good day too. There are always fewer patrols on Christmas Eve.'

In the animal comfort of rest and warmth, I had scarcely been listening to him. But, in spite of myself, his last words made me think of the bells, the rites, the traditions of peace time, the festival, and safety. Even the strange church at Collioure in the shape of a minaret, even the humble houses of the village were garnering at this moment the fruit ripened by the centuries. And here, in this camp of hunted vagabonds, a young woman was arranging a bed in the mud on which an exhausted man immediately fell asleep.

Almost without thinking I went over to her when she returned to the fire. She talked to me with complete candour.

'My husband is Spanish. He was a fighter pilot with the Republicans. He was wounded in the knee during the Civil War and took refuge in France. I met Carlos at Montpellier, where I was a student at the university. He has been dreaming for a long while past of fighting against the common enemy of all free people. Since the landing in North Africa, he can't bear it any longer. So I have come with him.'

She undid the scarf round her head and shook out her brown, damp hair before the fire. It made her look younger still.

'I wouldn't have come if it weren't for Carlos. But he believes what he believes so wholeheartedly.'

Was it the effect of the shadows and the glow of the wild fire animating the young woman's face? I do not know. It seemed to me to be the very expression of love itself. I asked her if she did not want to sleep.

'Impossible,' she said. 'The fire's so beautiful that it drives sleep away. All I needed was to take my shoes off.'

I suddenly saw that her bare feet, stretched out to the fire, were covered in blood.

'Carlos has friends in Figueras,' she murmured. 'They'll give me *espadrilles*.'

I did not know what to say.

She took a book from her haversack and began reading it by the light of the bonfire. It was Plato's *The Banquet*.

'I was reading philosophy at Montpellier,' she said as if by way of excuse. 'I want to continue my studies in Algeria.'

I went and lay down near José, who was talking in a low voice to big Juan. And because of that slight figure, lit by an outlaw's fire, because of her book and her love, that night has become part of my memories. Though I did not realise it then, it retains a greater sweetness and beauty than many other peaceful, happy Christmas Eves.

14
BESIDE THE THAMES

'I STARTED in Norway,' the Foreign Legion sergeant said to the sergeant of French Marines.

They were in one of the oldest pubs in London. It stood so close to the Thames that the big ships borne on the fog had for centuries passed close to its façade at high tide.

It was a Saturday evening. The survivors of the district, which had been a quarter destroyed by the bombs, gathered in this house which had been frequented for centuries by sailors, dockers, and the people of Wapping. Canadians, Americans, and men from the Commandos and the R.A.F. mingled with them. A big room gave on to the river. A pianola played ceaselessly. The customers drank and even danced. There were many women in uniform.

The Foreign Legion sergeant and the sergeant of Marines took their glasses into the outer room. It was quieter and less crowded. The light was in keeping with the dark patina of the panelling, smoky with age. A little grey monkey was asleep in a chair.

The two Frenchmen chose the darkest corner. They had met for the first time only a few minutes ago, but there was already a perfect understanding between them, a sense of security and friendship. They were the same type, strong, tough and wise. Fate had never found them wanting. That was why they had taken their drinks to talk peacefully in low voices in the shadow. I had followed them.

'You were talking about Norway...' said the sergeant of Marines.

'Yes, we were right up in the north...' the Foreign Legion sergeant said. 'We took Narvik and then we came away. All the big team were already there. Old Monclar, who is a general today, and Koenig, also a general, and Prince Amilac Vari, who was killed later at El Alamein. In France we had a terrible time, fighting without hope, without weapons or orders. We managed to embark at Brest.

Luckily the British were holding out, and de Gaulle was in England. Do you remember his appeal?'

'I heard it in Chad. It raised my morale at once,' said the sergeant of Marines.

The Foreign Legion sergeant nodded and went on: 'That 14 July 1940 when he reviewed us, we were only a handful of French under arms in all London, in all England, in the whole world. It was depressing, yet exciting. I don't know. I had fought previous campaigns for myself, for the Legion, but this was something different... I don't quite know how to explain it. It was like a new life, something quite different, a question of defending the honour of all Frenchmen. It was enough to make you weep.'

'That's right, that's right,' the sergeant of Marines hastened to agree. 'We all felt the same in Equatorial Africa when we began the war again only two months after *their* armistice.'

'I've heard about that,' the Foreign Legion sergeant remarked.

'It all happened in three days: Chad on 26 August, Cameroons on the 27th, and the Congo on the 28th. You were saying you had a good team in Norway. Well, we had Larminat, Leclerc, d'Ornano, Boislambert and Boissoudy. They were lions! They took back from Vichy enormous territories and millions of people.

'I was at Chad. I saw Colonel d'Ornano arrive at Fort-Lamy by air. He had gone to fetch General de Gaulle's representative from Lagos. What a welcome he got, my friend! The men on the airfield were mad with joy.

'In the Cameroons it was Leclerc and Boislambert who did the trick. They came to Nigeria from London. And from Nigeria they went to the Cameroons. They carried the governor with them.

'In the Congo, the de Lange battalion went out into the streets of Brazzaville at eleven o'clock in the morning. Captain de Boissoudy put the general, who refused to understand, under arrest. It was all over very quickly. Colonel de Larminat was the other side of the Congo, at Léopoldville. He crossed the river and took possession of the colony in the name of Free France.

'On the 26th, the 27th and the 28th, in Chad, the Cameroons and the Congo, we all felt that we were men again.'

'It took longer to take over Gabon.'

'I know,' said the Foreign Legion sergeant. 'I was there with Koenig.'

He stroked the little grey monkey who was looking at his two neighbours with intelligent, melancholy eyes.

'What a lot of these little beasts I saw at that time,' he said. 'In the jungle, along the rivers. Never have I had to go so far to fight. We had to cross the whole of Africa. People don't realise the distances! From Gabon, I went to Brazzaville. And from there we travelled for two months, covering more than three thousand miles.

'To begin with we set out in a paddle-boat. We went up the Congo for a fortnight. On both banks was the enormous equatorial forest. We sailed between two walls. Monkeys played about among the lower branches. We passed rafts and canoes. At times, there were clearings in the forest. Little men watched us go by. Tiny little men. It was the land of the pygmies.

'It was thus we reached Bangui. We continued our journey in trucks. Between Bangui and Fort-Archambeau, we passed through the cotton district. Then we came to a place called Abéché. In the old days it was the kingdom of the Sultans of Wadai. But now it's the frontier of the Sudan, which belongs to the British.

'We had plenty of time to find out about places. The trucks didn't go fast and the halts were long. But the hardest part of the journey still lay before us.

'Between Abéché and Khartoum lay twelve hundred miles of desert. An appalling track, nothing but soft sand. You know the sort of thing. A fierce sun, overheated engines and wheels sinking into the sand. You have to get out, dig away the sand, push the truck and look for firmer ground. You fall into another soft patch and it begins all over again. It would take us a day to do the distance you would cover in an hour on a good road. All the same, we reached Khartoum.

'After that, we travelled like tourists. We went by train to Port Sudan and then to Suakin. It's an old Arab town on the Red Sea, long abandoned by its inhabitants. A dead town. There are fine white houses, and lovely gardens. But the whole place is asleep and empty as if in a dream. From Suakin, we took ship for a little place in Eritrea. We had reached the battle at last.'

In the room giving on to the Thames the pianola continued to play dance tunes. The sergeant of Marines moved his head slightly in time to the music. But it was a purely unconscious reflex. He was not even hearing it.

'We had already been fighting,' he said. 'I was with a Chad infantry regiment. The men came from the Saras tribe. They're tall, broad-chested chaps with scarred faces. They look a bit frightening. Not very bright, but loyal and brave to the death.

'In January 1941, we set off for Chad. There was about a company of us with a few Goums and we were to harass the Italians in the oases round Mourzouk. Colonel d'Ornano was in command. He was a proper chap. A real desert soldier.

'You ought to have seen him. He was an old Sahara veteran, stood six feet six, wore a black eye-glass, and had a way with him which immediately impressed us all. He had the desert in his eyes and in his skin. He knew how to have a good time and he knew how to command and fight. A real chap. I was proud to be under his command. And I was proud, too, to be in the first French unit to go on operations against the enemy since the armistice.

'I thought: "The Italians came into this war like jackals to finish off France. They thought they had done it. Well, they'll see." That was what I was thinking as our trucks drove northwards.

'We had less distance to go to find the enemy than you had, but it was quite a long way all the same: Chad to cross, the Tibesti Mountains to go round and a bit of Libya to take. They're not easy countries.

'And that was why we managed to surprise the Italians so successfully, make a clean sweep of their oases and burn their aircraft. The only thing was that Colonel d'Ornano was killed at the beginning of the operations. As always, he was in the leading vehicle. In the attack, he had given up his place to the machine-gunner and was firing himself, lying on the petrol tins. We buried him with a New Zealand sergeant in a common grave before Mourzouk. We put their badges of rank on the blanket that covered them, and then set up a wooden cross with their names on it.

'Under the colonel's name we simply wrote: "Died for France." I think he must have been the first Frenchman to be killed in battle since the armistice.'

The two men fell silent for a while. Through the thick smoke that filled the little dark-panelled room, their eyes seemed to be seeing a distant, primitive grave.

'It's tough to lose a great leader,' the Foreign Legion sergeant said at last.

'But another great leader immediately appeared in Chad,' his companion went on. 'Today, the whole world knows Leclerc. He's the youngest and most famous French general. But, at the time I'm speaking of, his fame was only beginning.

'What was known of him? That he was a cavalry officer who had escaped from a prison camp in France and had joined General de Gaulle in London. He had never campaigned in the Sahara. He knew nothing about the desert. And we veterans of Chad, I must admit, had not much confidence in him. Well, after a few months, everyone was swearing by him. He was rather short, but wiry, had a Roman nose, a short moustache and piercing eyes. He could have led us anywhere. In fact, he did lead us wherever he wanted to.

'From the first affair at Koufra, we understood. No desert veteran was more indefatigable, no desert commander moved quicker than Colonel Leclerc who, at that time, was just thirty-five. The Koufra expedition took place shortly after Mourzouk and it certainly avenged Colonel d'Ornano.

'First, a light patrol in touring cars set off at full speed to sweep the approaches to the town. Leclerc, of course, went with it and during the battle, if necessary, he would take over a machine-gun himself. When the Italians had been properly stunned and bewildered, we besieged Koufra with very inferior forces to the enemy's.

'The En-Tag fort was formidable for the time and place. Its guns were set in the great walls, with an all-round field of fire. There were huge supplies of food and ammunition and an electric generating plant. In spite of all that, we took it in a week. On the 27th, the Italians surrendered. We took the garrison commander, his officers, his soldiers, anti-aircraft guns, mortars, machine-guns, tens of thousands of rounds of ammunition, trucks and light vehicles. And Leclerc made us present arms as the French flag with the Cross of Lorraine was hoisted over the fort.'

The Foreign Legion sergeant said: 'There really is such a thing as justice. The most cowardly, Mussolini's jackals as you called them just now, were punished first. You had scarcely finished at Koufra when we gave the Italians a knock in Eritrea.

'Each time I killed with rifle or grenade, with a bayonet thrust or a blow from the butt, I thought: "There's a Frenchman avenged, that's for refugees murdered on the roads." Besides, we had heard stories which had made our blood boil. Frenchmen had already died in that part of the world. Not in Eritrea itself, but in Abyssinia or in one of the neighbouring countries. Splendid Frenchmen. Men from the Aden Squadron.

'I'd heard so much about them that it's as if they had been my friends. They had come from Syria, Tunisia or the Far East, by air, ship or on foot. They had been assembled on the rock of Aden, the other side of the Red Sea. There were fifteen of them. There are two of them alive now. And one of the two was taken prisoner. The Italians condemned him to death because he was French. However, they didn't dare shoot him. But every night they told him it was going to happen next morning. They kept this up for months, till Addis was taken.

'Things like that, you know, enable you to bear anything.

'Nevertheless, things were not always very pleasant. Particularly at Queren. We were very high up, in a terrible mountain. It's a hellish country. Everything's as black as soot. Stones, lakes, rocks, even the dust. Endless precipices to climb and, at the top of them, Italian fortified positions. All they had to do was to put out a hand and drop grenade after grenade without any risk to themselves at all. We had three and a half pints of water per man per day.

'It was our chaplain, Father Malec, who did the unpleasant jobs under fire. He did not want to kill. That was not his trade. But he'd risk his skin to be useful. Father Malec had been a professor of philosophy in France.

'We had another professor with us. He was a doctor and his name was Frucheau. He was too old and hadn't the health for active service. Yet he did the whole campaign. At Queren, he was operating in the front line, at an altitude of 6,000 feet, two days' march from our starting base. He saved a lot of men's lives. We needed him. There were a great many casualties. The position was very favourable to the Italians.

'But, later on, we were able to manoeuvre. We cut the road between Queren and Asmara. After a forced march of ten hours, taking dozens of officers and hundreds of soldiers prisoner. Old Cazaud was in command. He's a general today. His appearance is against him. He's short and grey and very modest. But I've never seen a calmer, wiser man under fire. You'd think he was playing draughts, making his plans at his ease.

'Then we cut the road from Asmara to Massowa, that's to say between the capital and the great port of Eritrea. It was a motorised column and we moved quickly. We prevented demolitions. Those that had already damaged the road the Italians had to repair themselves. By doing this we saved the main force of the British troops a day. At that moment, this was of the first importance. I needn't tell you that we took more prisoners. They already numbered more than our whole force. But all this was of little importance. Massowa had still to be taken.

'The Legion was to attack the three forts which were the key to the town: Moncallo, Vittorio-Emmanuel and Humberto. They were well sited, strongly armed and had large garrisons. There were 120 big guns. It seemed to me that our officers themselves thought success impossible. They advanced in front, and we followed them, and we took the forts one after the other. There again, old Cazaud showed what he could do, as did Captain Amilac Vari, the Georgian prince.

'When the forts had surrendered, Monclar went alone into Massowa, where he ordered the Italian police to disarm the Italian soldiers. They obeyed. Meanwhile, some of our motor-cyclists and two truck-loads of Legionaries made a reconnaissance through the town. They took the central hotel. There were ninety officers in it. They surrendered.

'Their generals had fled. But a non-commissioned officer came to fetch his general's kit. The general was the garrison commander. The non-commissioned officer led us to him. We captured him with thirty officers. The general led us to the admiral, and the admiral to the Italian commander-in-chief in Eritrea. We captured them and their 440 officers and 11,000 soldiers.

'We of the Legion numbered only a little over 1,000. With us, we had only the 3rd Company of a battalion of Marines. But that company alone took 1,900 Italians prisoner. Captain Savet commanded it. A former Dominican, and a lion. He was the first to reach the harbour at Massowa. He was killed later at Bir-Hakeim. The Italian flags fell five times that day to the French.

'General de Gaulle had already come to see us one day in Eritrea before the great battle. He came to see us again in Palestine, where we were resting, after the campaign. He reviewed us. The general doesn't show much what he's thinking, you know. But that time we felt he was not displeased with us. We could go forward with high hearts.'

The Foreign Legion sergeant suddenly got to his feet and went to the bar above which hung a little stuffed crocodile together with many souvenirs of sea voyages. He drank a large glass of beer and came back to sit in the dark corner near the door, where his friend was waiting for him. He brought two bottles with him.

'It's odd,' said the Foreign Legion sergeant, 'but every time I think of the Libyan campaign, I have a perpetual thirst as if I were in the desert, with sand storms that dry your throat up and dreams all the time of good cold beer. When you've led that sort of life for months and months, it has a permanent effect on your mind and body.'

'And in spite of the thirst and the hard knocks, one looks back on it with a certain regret,' said the sergeant of Marines.

'What I liked best during the advance to El Mechili, then in the retreat, and again during the four months we spent at Bir-Hakeim before the attack,' said the Foreign Legion sergeant, 'were the Jock columns.

'This was the name the British gave to the big reconnaissance patrols in no-man's-land, which was sometimes sixty miles or more wide. You set off in a Bren-carrier, armed with a gun. There were two of you in it and you set off into the desert like lords to find the Germans and shoot quicker than they could.

'For it was not only with the Italians we had to do now, and because of the Germans we felt more than ever that we were fighting for France.

'We had a number of successes on these patrols. But perhaps the greatest was brought off by one of your chaps, Sergeant-Major Le Pelletier of the Marines.

'One morning, Le Pelletier set off in a carrier, he on the gun and a young chap of twenty driving. They patrolled through and over the sandhills. Eventually they reached the crest of a hill and found themselves face to face with a German vehicle which had come up the farther slope. There weren't more than a dozen yards between them. Le Pelletier fired his gun. It jammed. Le Pelletier jumped down and shot the German driver and gunner with his rifle. At that moment a German armoured vehicle appeared. It fired. A shell hit Le Pelletier in the foot, leaving it attached to his leg merely by a piece of skin. Le Pelletier took out his knife and cut the piece of skin, then he hopped back to the carrier and came home. The Germans were so surprised to see him operate on himself that they forgot to go on firing.

'This was the way we spent our time till Bir-Hakeim.'

'Bir-Hakeim!' the sergeant of Marines said with respect.

'Yes, Bir-Hakeim!' repeated the Foreign Legion sergeant.

He rubbed his hands together with an embarrassed air and went on: 'I'm not going to try to bluff you; while we were there, none of us thought we were doing anything extraordinary.'

'It's always like that,' the sergeant of Marines remarked.

'We only carried out our orders,' the Foreign Legion sergeant said. 'And Koenig gave the orders. So we carried them out with a good heart. Today, everyone says "General Koenig," but to us he remains just Koenig. He's a veteran of the Legion. We knew him before Norway. No one has such a taking smile. He's always happy. Everything's always going well. Everything will always come out all right. One would do anything for him. It's easy to understand.

'You know the story. The first assaults repulsed, Rommel's ultimatum to which Koenig gave the proper reply, the charges by the German tanks which cost them dear, and the Stukas which didn't frighten us, and our counter-attacks, and how we freed a large number of British prisoners, and finally the break-out when, on superior orders, we had to evacuate Bir-Hakeim.'

'What I'd like to have seen,' said the sergeant of Marines, 'was the expression on the faces of Rommel's envoys, when they were sent about their business.'

'It was like a film,' said the Foreign Legion sergeant.

He began laughing.

'There are some good stories about Bir-Hakeim,' he went on. 'The best I know happened to Captain Morel. He fought, like his men, with grenades, and half-naked because it was pretty hot. One day, he took an Italian colonel prisoner: "I can only surrender to an officer," the Italian said. "I am an officer," Captain Morel replied. The Italian colonel looked at the bearded, half-naked devil, and refused to believe him. And the captain had to go and fetch his cap.'

It was the sergeant of Marines' turn to laugh.

'Captain Morel was the hell of a chap,' said the Foreign Legion sergeant. 'I must tell you that at that moment he had already been wounded four times: once in Eritrea and three times at Bir-Hakeim. He was wounded a fifth time at El Alamein. He always refused to be evacuated.

'But there were even better examples than that. I saw with my own eyes Captain de Boissoudy, who had lost his legs in Syria, commanding his infantry battalion at Bir-Hakeim from a chair carried by two negroes.'

'Wait a moment,' said the sergeant of Marines. 'Is that the same Boissoudy who did the trick at Brazzaville? Is he one of our chaps, in the Colonial army?'

'That's right,' said the Foreign Legion sergeant. 'No one hesitated at Bir-Hakeim. I remember a 75 with a black gun-team. They were firing at tanks over open sights. The gun-layer was killed. The loader replaced him and fell. No 3 took his turn. He was knocked out by a bullet in the head. No 4 aimed and fired for several minutes. Then he fell on the others. So No 5, the last of the team, calmly pushed his comrades' bodies out of the way with his foot, and set about pulling the string.

'There was also the Pacific battalion. It had come from the other side of the world to die. I knew fabulously wealthy planters among them. No one could compare with them on patrols and ambushes. They were born hunters, you see. They never came back without a necklace of Italian or German ears.

'No one hesitated. That was why Commandant Savet, the former Dominican, who had taken 1,900 prisoners at Massawa, was killed. That was why a young chap of eighteen, and who looked as if he were fifteen, jumped into a truck that had been set on fire by a bomb from a Stuka to remove a case of fuses that might blow the whole thing up. It burst against his body. He had one arm blown off and the other damaged. The explosion blew all his clothes off. He had nothing left but the belt of his shorts. He made a tourniquet of it at his shoulder. He was found hours later in the desert. He survived. He doesn't like the story being mentioned. He doesn't feel he did anything extraordinary either.

'It was only after it was all over that we learnt the noise Bir-Hakeim had made in the world,' the Foreign Legion sergeant went on. 'There was the signal to Koenig from General de Gaulle. There was the wonderful welcome the British gave us when we reached their lines. And we weren't very handsome to look at either: unshaven, unwashed, in rags, riding in every sort of truck, some even captured from the Germans. We were frightened to look at each other.

'When Koenig reviewed us for the first time, we still weren't much to look at. He was already rested and smiling. Of course, it didn't take us long to get back into form. And for ceremonial parades, you could have seen us polishing and scrubbing as if for a parade in the Sidi-Bel-Abbès barracks. General de Larminat came to hand out decorations. General Alexander came to have a look at us. We did what we could not to lose face.

'We were shown to everybody. We were taken all over the place. We were the chaps of Bir-Hakeim. The whole thing was even rather exaggerated.'

The sergeant of Marines shook his pipe and said: 'It was enough to give you swollen heads.'

'It was,' his companion agreed. 'However, something happened at that time which put us in our places. A comrade received, through England, letters from France which, it appeared, had come by somewhat unusual channels. They were letters from his wife and his brother. They both told him of the resistance they were making to the Germans in a certain organisation.

'They told of sabotage, demonstrations, stories of irregular troops, of friends imprisoned and shot. With the letters were a few secretly printed newspapers. Well, my lad, when we thought of the courage required merely to print and distribute those newspapers, we felt pretty small. And we fought with still greater determination at El Alamein and then on the road to Tripoli.'

'There's more than one road to Tripoli,' the sergeant of Marines remarked. 'While you were following the coast, we, with Leclerc, were marching by the Tibesti and the Fezzan.'

'That was a wonderful thing to do,' said the Foreign Legion sergeant. 'No one would have believed it possible to march from Chad to the Mediterranean.'

'No one except Leclerc,' said the sergeant of Marines. 'He believed in it, and he did it. And we, behind him. One needs to have taken part in that campaign to know what a real leader can undertake and bring to success.

'The Italians and even the Germans had declared we could not get through. Between Fort-Lamy and Tripoli there are the Tibesti and the Fezzan. The Tibesti is an appalling place. Desert, with peaks running up to 9,000 feet. And these mountains are hundreds of miles in depth; and there's not a single water-point. Then there was the Fezzan, where the Italians had fortified every hill, blocked every track and armed every oasis. Well, in under forty days, we had broken through, carried all the strong-points and reached the sea.

'Of course, we had trained hard before setting out. And we had had a bit of practice in the raids on Koufra and Mourzouk. We had already patrolled in the Fezzan. But the big expedition was tough in another way.

'The column, which was completely motorised, consisted of Tibesti camel-corps, Chad infantry, as well as of young Frenchmen come from England. I take my hat off to them. It was a terrible ordeal for recruits. But they came through it like the others. And there was not a single supply depôt, not a single drop of water till the central Fezzan. We had to carry everything and go on short rations. That was why we did it so quickly. And for speed, you can rely on Leclerc. That man's like lightning.

'We crossed the Tibesti without being seen. It seemed absolutely incredible and impossible. On 1 January, we made contact with the dumbfounded Italians. We knocked them arse over tip, and the pursuit began. Oum el Araneb, Gatroum, Brack, Sebah and finally Mourzouk, all the positions were either carried or surrendered. There were masses of booty and prisoners.

'General Leclerc took possession of the Fezzan in the name of Fighting France. He appointed a governor. He added a new territory to the French Empire. Then he went on. His advance-guards entered Tripoli at the same time as the Eighth Army.'

The Foreign Legion sergeant sighed.

'I'd have liked to have been with you in that business. But one can't be everywhere.'

'That's right,' said the sergeant of Marines. 'When I think that my comrades are marching on Tunisia . . .'

'Mine too,' said the Foreign Legion sergeant.

'One must be sensible about it. We shall all meet again in France,' said the sergeant of Marines. 'At least, those of us who haven't been killed.'

'Of course,' said the Foreign Legion sergeant. They ceased talking and drank in a serene silence.

The Foreign Legion sergeant was killed before Colmar.

The sergeant of Marines went as far as Berchtesgarden and brought back a few souvenirs from Hitler's lair.

He sometimes shows them in the little café he keeps in Corrèze.

15
EN PASSANT

It was a fine, light, spacious house and lay some thirty miles from London, among smooth lawns and magnificent old trees. A Frenchman called Colonel Remy lived in it. In 1940 he had founded and organised one of the first intelligence networks in the service of General de Gaulle and, after running mortal risks in France for three years, he was now directing from England one of those complex, secret organisations which so powerfully assisted the Allies at the time of the landings.

The house was always overcrowded, for it gave shelter to people arriving from France and to others on their way there, as well as to the wives and children both of the men who were there and of those who had gone. One found there an extraordinary combination of courage, faith, adventure and of nursery.

It was in this house, at the beginning of summer 1944, that I first met Mary. It was, of course, a pseudonym. But, since he made it famous, why seek another name?

Mary was a young man of medium height, with an exceptionally high, wide and prominent forehead. Beneath his forehead were dark, thoughtful and softly luminous eyes. Mary's voice had great charm, both because of its tenderness and a slight, musical Burgundian accent. He moved with a sort of calm determination.

His appearance did not at first attract my attention. The conversation at Remy's table was fascinating. The men, and often the women, who came to it had fantastic stories to tell. Their usual means of transport were parachute, secret aircraft and boats. Their experiences were enough to fill innumerable novels. Mary seemed withdrawn and listened absently and in silence. When dinner was over, he went off without a word to smoke in the bay window which gave on to the dark lawns.

My host pointed to the solitary figure and said: 'I think that's the man who, individually and physically, has done most damage to the

Germans in France. I shan't tell you how: you probably wouldn't believe me. Find out for yourself!'

I took his advice and, from unquestionable sources and authentic documents, discovered what follows.

In 1939, when the war began, Mary was a member of the fire-brigade of Chalon-sur-Saône. He went to the front as a lieutenant and spent the winter and the spring near Sierck on the Luxemburg frontier. The great collapse took him from Sierck to Perpignan where he was demobilised. On 14 July 1940, he was back in Chalon-sur-Saône.

At that moment France was stunned by her misfortune. Hesitant, baffled, bewildered and confounded, people were beginning to learn how to live again. With most of them, thought and emotion were suspended, anaesthetised by an enormous, helpless amazement and a confused distress. Mary was one of the very few men at that time who pursued the struggle against the enemy without a moment's pause. For him there was no armistice, no truce, no waiting. His job and his knowledge of the country enabled him to move easily on both sides of the line which divided France into two zones and passed through Chalon-sur-Saône. Mary devoted all his energies and resources to helping escaped prisoners of war, who were at that time arriving in great numbers, to cross the demarcation line.[1]

He would put two or three of them into the boot of a car, which he drove himself, and put them out in unoccupied territory. By this means and others, he took some 4,500 escaped prisoners across the frontier to liberty. It is a fantastic figure. And yet it is accurate, as the whole of Mary's story throughout more than four years is at once accurate and fantastic.

But Mary's passengers were not only prisoners of war. One day, he had the occasion to help the leader of an organisation that was working for General de Gaulle. By this means, Mary made contact with London.

A radio-transmitter—one of the first—was placed at his disposal with a radio-operator nicknamed 'Little Louis.' Mary installed them

[1] In this task, and in all the others he undertook later, Mary had as his inseparable companion a childhood friend called Jean Goujon. I met him also in London. He had the look of a peasant and a poacher, intelligent, wise, cunning and quietly courageous. Like Mary, he survived four years of extraordinary adventures.

in the neighbourhood of Chalon-sur-Saône. Little Louis was in charge of transmissions. Mary gathered and assembled information.

At this time, there were very few secret radios in France. A great part of the country had no means of liaison with London except through Mary's and Little Louis' transmitter. As a result he sent messages for twelve and sometimes fourteen hours a day.

Knowing as one does the appalling dangers of sending secret messages even for a tenth of this time, it is clear that these men were more or less condemning themselves to death. And, indeed, having worked for much longer than the probabilities warranted, Little Louis was arrested, tortured and shot.

Mary had his car riddled with bullets on several occasions, jumped from a burning mill, avoided a dozen traps and was at last seized by a number of police as he arrived at the Gare de Lyon in Paris. The police were Frenchmen belonging to Doriot's party and worked officially for the Gestapo. They threw Mary into a car and beat him up before they even questioned him. They went on hitting him till they reached the Cherche-Midi.

Mary remained perfectly calm throughout the journey. He had only one thought: to get rid of the more-than-confidential papers hidden in his tobacco pouch and the rubber stamps for forging documents concealed inside a cold chicken. And he succeeded precisely because they were beating him up. His torturers were not paying attention to what he was doing with his hands.

In the prison, the PPF men stripped Mary to the waist and redoubled their brutality. They said: 'You're done for. We know who you are, what you've done, and what you've come to do. You were given away as you left.'

It was true. A German officer in Chalon-sur-Saône suspected Mary. He had signalled to the Paris authorities.

'You must tell us everything you know!' Doriot's men repeated as they beat Mary. 'Everything: names and addresses.'

Under the blows and kicks battering his face and body that were already covered with wounds, Mary was calculating his chances. To escape from the Cherche-Midi was impossible. But outside, there might be a chance.

'I've got only one contact in Paris,' he said at last. 'But I don't know the chap's name. And I can't remember the address. You've beaten me so much you've driven it out of my head. I'd recognise the house if I went there.'

And Mary, his torso still naked and bloody, his face one bruise, led the police to a street in Montmartre. In fact, he did have a friend there, but he knew that he was away. Nevertheless, it was in fear and trembling that he knocked at his door. His friend might have returned earlier than was expected. There was no answer. The door was forced open, and the flat ransacked. Nothing important was found.

While this was going on, Mary had not had a moment's opportunity to escape. The police had kept him covered with their pistols all the time.

After the search, Mary was not taken back to the Cherche-Midi. Even today, he does not know why. Perhaps the PPF men were bored with beating him up. Perhaps they were attracted by the Montmartre nightclubs. Perhaps they had plans for the next day of which Mary knew nothing. However that may be, they took Mary to a wretched little hotel in the neighbourhood which was occupied by the Gestapo. They handed him over to a German sentry.

The soldier took Mary up to a room. He paid no particular attention to the half-naked, exhausted, panting prisoner whose face was scarcely human. Suddenly, he was forcibly butted in the stomach. Mary dashed down the stairs and rushed out into the dark street. He did not get far. At the first cross-roads, he was arrested by members of the Paris police force.

'I'm not a criminal,' Mary said. 'I'm a patriot. I've just escaped from the Germans. You won't give me up?'

The police were not disposed to believe a half-naked man with a battered face. They were about to take him to the police station when Mary remembered that a Special Commissaire of one of the great Paris railway stations was a member of his network. He asked the police to take him to this man. They agreed, but the commissaire was not in his office. They had to telephone. He lived in a suburb. The wait was interminable. At last, the commissaire arrived and identified Mary.

A little while later, on orders, Mary and his friend Jean Gougon, secretly crossed the Pyrenees on their way to London. This was in November 1942. I asked Mary one day whether, at that time, he had attacked Germans.

'Of course,' he said with a sort of astonished gentleness. 'Of course. Any I caught wandering about and at a disadvantage. I never missed those. Of course, just *en passant*.'

Mary crossed the Pyrenees, and the Spanish trap—the only one in which he was ever caught—closed about him. He suffered the fate of thousands of Frenchmen who took the same road. He was imprisoned in filthy, verminous prisons, and in the starvation camp of Miranda.

This lasted seven months. On being freed, he came to England. He went through a complete course of parachute-jumping, explosives and all light weapons. He was then parachuted back into France and landed without mishap.

Thereupon, Mary's life took on a truly epic quality. His mission was to put out of use a series of power stations, high-tension grids, cables and power installations that were essential to the German war industry and communications.

The plan was so vast, difficult and dangerous that, had Mary carried out only the half of it, he would have done something wholly exceptional. He carried it completely through with incredible speed and efficiency; nor did he limit himself to this. How can one describe, as one should, Mary's adventures? Mere enumeration can give but little idea of them. Only the details can give a sense of the effort, ingenuity, courage and risk of each enterprise. Only minute, technical truth can overcome astonishment and carry conviction.

One night, by sheer enthusiasm and insistence, I forced Mary to recount (which was not a thing he liked doing) some of his memories. By the time I left him, I was utterly astonished and bewildered. My brain refused to retain so many extraordinary stories. My imagination was defeated by the accounts he gave in a simple, straightforward, rather singsong voice.

For weeks, wherever Mary went, thunderbolts went with him. Power stations collapsed in flames, huge pylons fell and magazines blew up. This man, with his wide forehead and brown, bright eyes, was inhabited by the daemon of fire and annihilation. This secret, hunted man struck in a dozen different places, sometimes in the same day: Le Creusot, Limoges, Rheims, Lille, Paris. . . And everywhere there were guards and sentries and, more dangerous still, traitors working for the enemy. Mary got through, his car filled with grenades, dynamite, fuses, plastic bombs, made his plans, carried them out and went off again, while German corpses remained to keep watch over the smoking ruins.

On one occasion, his plan failed. He began again that same night, calculating that the enemy would not expect such great audacity.

Afterwards, he sent a brief report to London. It said nothing of his constantly renewed methods, his labours, his determination, nor of the risks he ran. It merely read: 'Objective attained.'

But all this was not enough for Mary.

Over and above his mission, he was doing work no one had asked or expected him to do. He did it, as he said, '*en passant.*'

He would be driving along a road. He would be told of traitors, militia or informers. He would blow them up together with their house. He would enter a town and the chief of the Gestapo's house, standing somewhat apart, would be pointed out to him. He would lay an ambush with his team, which never consisted of more than three companions. He would kill the chief of the Gestapo, seize his papers, and drive off in his car. The German sentries would present arms. He killed—'*en passant*'—with his own hand more than sixty enemy or enemy agents.

When he had completed his mission, he returned to England by secret aircraft.

In London he was given new weapons and new instructions and was parachuted back into France.

This second mission of Mary's was even more important than the first. It was to destroy locks and weirs in such a way as to debar the Germans from using the rivers to reach the Mediterranean. This was the route they used for pocket-submarines and other even more secret little war craft.

Mary (with Jean Goujon) carried out this task so well that some British authorities maintained that, without this operation, the landings in Italy could not have succeeded. Meanwhile Mary was still carrying on the work he did *en passant.*

One of his exploits took him to the neighbourhood of the Mailly camp. He remembered that new armoured units had arrived there and that, as a result, the whole internal dispositions had been altered. He had no orders whatever to investigate this. And he had no assistance with which to undertake an investigation. Indeed, it was not his business.

Nevertheless, he went to the guardroom and asked to see the camp commander. Among his false papers, Mary carried the card of an inspector of police. He showed it to the German officer and said: 'I am told there are terrorists in your area and, in order to assist your protective measures, I have come to find out what dispositions you have made.'

The camp commander was delighted. He liked the 'good' French who understood where the salvation of Europe lay. He took Mary round the whole camp. He did better. In his office, he showed him a detailed plan of the positions of units, batteries and pill-boxes. And, being called away, he left Mary alone with the plan to study it at his leisure.

Mary copied the document and left. A few days later the copy was in London. Mary arrived there shortly after.

On 7 July 1944, Mary was again parachuted into France by night. He now had a quite different mission. He was no longer an individual saboteur with small teams at his command. He had come to set up the military organisation, under the guns and machine-guns of the enemy, of two vast districts, whose men he was to lead into battle.

To relate Mary's proceedings, I can do no better than give some extracts from the report sent to General de Gaulle by Mary's immediate chief. No style can be more appropriate than its spare directness.

> I have the honour to report on the work carried out by Commandant Mary, the departmental military delegate for the Rhône and the Loire and Chief of the FFI for the same region.
>
> He was parachuted into occupied territory on 7 July 1944 with four officers from London.
>
> The situation in the Rhône was as follows: 2,000 men in the maquis, of which 400 were normally armed, fifteen groups of various affiliations who obeyed only the leaders of their groups.
>
> From 7 July to 15 August, travelling about his district day and night, personally transporting and distributing the arms he received at night, Mary attended every parachute operation. In record time, he succeeded in arming 4,000 men. He won the confidence of his men by taking part with them in innumerable

operations, which he personally directed. Some of the principal of these were as follows:

1. Destruction of the Mulatière dam. Personnel: 3 men.
2. The burning of a train loaded with straw at Limonest.
3. Destruction of a petrol train destined for the Luftwaffe and heavily manned by Germans 3 kilometres from Vienne. Personnel: 10 men.
4. Attack on the Tarare station and tunnel. Everything that could move was sent into the tunnel. Five locomotives and three goods trains were derailed in the tunnel. Twenty-two Germans were killed. Personnel: 60 men.
5. The Bully tunnel. Destruction of a train carrying tanks on its way to Normandy. Fifteen men killed, including a colonel. Personnel: 20 men.
6. The Givors tunnel. Destruction of a train carrying armoured cars and another carrying Tiger tanks.

Between 7 July and 2 September, daily attacks on German convoys on all the roads leading to Lyon.

Preparation of the plan of attack on Lyon with the reinforcements from the Ardèche, the Drôme, the Ain and the Vercors.

Eight days before the taking of Lyon, Commandant Mary had nearly 15,000 men under his command. No German train or convoy passed without being attacked. On some days over 1,000 Germans were put out of action. A single group of SAS annihilated over 2,000 Germans in four days. Saint-Étienne was liberated and all the works and factories protected. Bourguin and its stores were seized and an immense booty taken. La Valbonne and Sathenay also fell as well as the forts surrounding Lyon.

Commandant Mary persuaded the FTP to sign an agreement recognising him as sole chief of the FFI. Thanks to this immense work, de Lattre's army entered Lyon without meeting a single German.

Commandant Mary, during the period from July '40 till now, has been awarded:

The Croix de Guerre with three citations in Army orders

The Croix de la Libération

The Military Cross

The Distinguished Service Order

He has also been recommended three times for the Légion

d'Honneur: first in October '43; second in February '44; third in May '44.

To develop this report as it should be done, to give a true picture of those few weeks, a film would be necessary—a film of parachute operations, ambushes, supply organisation for food and equipment, the training of whole battalions, constant liaison with the French organisations in London, the destruction of enemy material and personnel, the breaking of communications, the establishing of hospitals in the maquis, constant, sudden, audacious and lucky attacks, and the execution of Militia and traitors. And in that film, Mary, on whose head there was a price, would be everywhere, at Lyon, Saint-Étienne, Roanne, in the villages, in the maquis, on the parachuting grounds where the containers of arms and ammunition fell, on the roads, making his way through road-blocks, passing German trucks, on the railways cutting the lines, enthusing everyone, directing operations and killing whole groups of Germans. And the film would be true, and the portrait accurate.

When Mary began to organise and train the men placed under his command, most of them had no weapons. They were impatient and excited and complained of being able to do nothing.

'You don't need to be armed to do useful work,' Mary would tell them; and, unarmed himself, he would lead a group to saw through lines and cables. And he would lead another group to a guarded train carrying straw to the Germans, light his lighter and set fire to it. After that, the young men of the maquis were ready to do anything on an order from Mary.

On 22 July 1944, a petrol train which supplied the Luftwaffe and which the Germans were constantly moving, was reported by the railway workers to be parked for the night in a little station three kilometres from Vienne. Mary decided to attack it. He selected from the nearest maquis ten young men who had never been under fire. They were under the command of Captain Ferrier. They left at about four o'clock in the morning in a car and a van. The train consisted of forty-six tanker-wagons full of petrol and four wagons in which the soldiers guarding it lived—approximately eighty men.

Mary's two vehicles reached the train at 0545 hours. The van, to mislead the enemy, went to the end of the train and Ferrier opened fire. The Germans were taken by surprise and replied at random.

Meanwhile Mary took aim with his bazooka, an anti-tank weapon which normally had a mask to protect the firer from the flame of the explosion. But Mary's bazooka, owing to a parachute accident, had no mask. At each shot a jet of flame burnt his cheek. But what did he care? He had never had so splendid a target. He began on the wagons full of enemy soldiers. The wagons blew up and the soldiers were thrown into the air like puppets. Mary moved along the train and blew up tank after tank. It was all over in ten minutes. Mary had half his face burnt but forty-six wagons of petrol were burning, eighty Germans were dead and the heat melted the lines over sixty yards. Mary's men had escaped without a scratch.

But of all Mary's adventures, there was one which was even more astonishing.

Shortly after being parachuted, he was surprised by the Gestapo in the flat in Lyon where he was hiding. He just had time to jump out of the window and make his escape. He was safe, but he had left his codes and plans in his room.

He hurried off to a friend who was a lieutenant in the Customs.

'Give me a uniform, quick!' he said.

'What for?' his friend asked.

'I've no time, a uniform!' replied Mary.

And Mary, with a price on his head, returned to the apartment where the agents of the Gestapo were. They did not recognise him in the uniform and cap of a Customs Officer.

'I have orders to search the place over a fraud concerning coffee,' Mary said.

The Germans protested. They were the masters.

'I shall carry out my orders!' Mary said.

He pushed the Gestapo men out of the way, and they were so astonished they let him in. Mary went to his room, took his plans and codes from their hiding place, concealed them under his tunic together with a small English bomb, ready-primed. If the Germans opposed his departure, he would blow himself up with them and the documents. But the Germans did not prevent his leaving.

I had been told of this episode in London. Later, I heard it from Mary himself. When he had finished relating it, he added: 'I was frightened—so frightened my knees would scarcely carry me. The fools didn't even notice.'

16
THE FIRING SQUAD

I MET him on a summer's day in 1943 on the airfield at Marrakesh.

I had arrived from Algiers in a French aircraft, and had landed there to leave for England in an American bomber. The preparations for departure took a long time. But the wait did not bore me. The marvellous sky, the peaks of the Atlas mountains, the movements of the Moroccan workmen, a sense of lightness, and leisure, all contributed to deprive time of its value and to hold thought in suspense.

Suddenly, I was no longer seeing the sky and the mountains and my reverie was cut short. Two men—a commandant and a captain—joined the little group who were to leave in the Flying Fortress. They each had the sort of appearance which was bound to attract the most distrait and wandering mind.

They were both tall and broad, and had the powerful necks, massive shoulders and deep chests of heavy athletes. They held their heads proudly and defiantly high and turned unblinkingly to the heat of the sun faces that were still young but marked, moulded and, as one might say, signed by their epic lives. In the lines of their faces and in their expressions, there were the ruggedness and the poetry of the soldier, the bandit, the corsair and the inspired adventurer.

They wore no decorations on their khaki shirts, only the insignia of Free France.

The commandant, with the brow and mane of a bison, had lost his right arm. The amputation was recent and a black stain showed through the bandages which enveloped the stump just below the shoulder. His companion walked with the help of a stick.

I cannot remember how the conversation began. But I do remember that, from the very first words spoken, there was that tone of confidence and comradeship which is more important even than the words. I was fascinated by these two men. They had read three or four of my books and had a liking for some of my heroes, without realising that they themselves wholly surpassed the characters I had been able tc imagine and describe in the intensity of their forcefulness and the power of their high destiny.

Huge flies were settling on the dark, sticky fluid emanating from the commandant's wound. When the swarm became too greedy, he shook his stump like a broken aileron.

'Aren't you afraid of infection?' I asked him.

'That's all nonsense,' he said in his hoarse, rumbling voice. 'There are hospitals in London, aren't there?'

'He's got a hide like an elephant,' the captain muttered. 'He's already recovered from seventeen wounds.'

'That's right,' the commandant allowed. 'At least, if you only count those inflicted on me by humans.'

'Oh, of course. If it's a question of horns, claws and teeth, we're all square,' his companion said.

We were suddenly deafened by the thunder of the four engines. The travellers hauled themselves on board the bomber.

Except in the crew's compartment, there were no seats. Instead, there were suitcases, bedding-rolls, tin trunks and valises. You could sit where you liked and next to whom you pleased. The conversation we had begun on the airfield continued during the flight.

The flight lasted eight hours and I was able to learn a good deal about my new friends by getting them to talk about each other.

They had known each other extremely well for a long time, and each was aware of the strength and sincerity of the other. They had both spent the most important part of their lives in Equatorial Africa. Character and temperament, deprived of the amenities, conventions, artificialities and façades of civilisation, no doubt became nakedly apparent.

They came from different backgrounds. The commandant was a schoolmaster. The captain, an engineer from a well-known college, had gone to Africa as an employee of a public works company. But they both had a passion for the jungle, the wilds, the primitive tribes, daring expeditions and, above all, the more dangerous forms of hunting. They travelled continually about the country, and were known both to whites and blacks as the best shots in those immense territories.

The engineer had soon left his employment to become a gold

prospector, a carrier, a planter, and a slayer of buffaloes, lions and elephants. The restrictions on big-game shooting had no weight with him. He poached skins and ivory happily. The schoolmaster did the same.

In 1939, they were called up in Africa. The defeat came too quickly for them to have been able to take any part in the fighting in France. The news of the armistice left them stunned, dazed and incredulous. But then followed the appeal of 18 June. They were not the men to accept defeat or bow to the yoke. They could breathe again. Both Chad and the Congo rallied to the unknown general who had spoken from London. The two hunters were the first volunteers. An army was being formed. They were sent out into the wilds to recruit.

The conversation had reached this point when the bomber began to lose height as we approached the English coast. We could already see its outline in the warm mist of evening.

'The recruiting presented no problems,' one of my companions (I don't remember which of them) said. 'You went from village to village with your native soldiers. You looked for robust negroes, and the Saras, for instance, are magnificent chaps, almost giants. You selected the finest. And to make sure you got them all safely back, you attached them in file with slip-knots round their necks. If one of them got out of line he strangled the others.'

'But . . .' I protested.

The two officers exchanged an amused and indulgent glance. The commandant waved his stump and said: 'Yes, I know. The law. The liberty of the subject. But it was for law and liberty we were recruiting them, wasn't it?'

'Like slaves,' I could not help saying.

'Possibly,' the captain quietly agreed. 'Possibly. But give the slaves—as we did—plenty of food, good uniforms, nice red hats and new weapons—and they become proud soldiers, happy to be alive and to fight.'

'Heroes, I assure you,' the commandant went on. 'Fezzan, Ethiopia, Eritrea . . .'

'Syria and Bir-Hakeim,' the captain concluded.

The two men knew what they were talking about. They had been in all these battles.

We were about to land.

'See you soon,' the commandant said.

'We're bound to meet in London,' the captain added.

His words startled me. He had spoken in Russian.

He smiled at my surprise and went on: 'My family comes from Russia and, like you, I haven't forgotten my native tongue.'

The bomber was bowling along the runway.

The commandant's name was Bourgoin and the captain's Conus.

Bourgoin was on his way to take command of the Free French parachute battalion. A year later, at the time of the Allied landings, he was to parachute into France at its head. The one-armed colonel was to become a legendary figure.

Less is known about Captain Conus' activities.

I did, in fact, often meet him again.

We had mutual friends among the little society that the Free French formed in London. For instance, Guy de Boissoudy who had lost a leg in Syria and made a parachute-jump with a wooden leg to win a bet of a case of champagne.

Also Claude de Boislambert, another great big-game hunter in peacetime, who had tried to raise Dakar in the summer of 1940, had been captured by Vichy partisans, imprisoned in the filthy prisons of Sénégal, and then transferred to a French prison from which he made a famous escape and managed to reach England.

I learnt from them why and how Conus, the engineer, soon after his arrival in Africa, had abandoned a safe, highly-paid job with brilliant prospects for the risks and uncertainties of a hand-to-mouth existence.

A director of his company, who had come out on a tour of inspection, spoke to him in a tone to which he took exception. Conus had hit the director. It had been a purely reflex action. He had not taken his own Herculean strength into consideration. According to some, the blow had sent the victim to hospital; according to others, to the grave. Conus had taken to the jungle till things blew over.

I learnt, too, how Lieutenant Conus had become famous in the column Leclerc led from Chad to Tunisia. He had invented a method of mounting 75 guns on trucks. This had been a great contribution to the victory.

But it was walking at night through London that I really got to know Conus. His wounded knee was better and he no longer needed a stick. He walked with a long, light, silent and indefatigable stride. One realised he could cover miles without tiring.

Was it due to the dark of the blackout, to the ruins vaguely outlined in the bombed areas, or to our similar origins that Conus emerged on these occasions from his usual reserve? I listened to him each time with renewed astonishment.

He was not at all the mere soldier of fortune, the rough adventurer, all of a piece and of a single texture, I had thought him on the airfield at Marrakesh and in the aircraft. Certainly, his toughness, physical strength, hazardous life, legendary hunting and campaigning were all strictly true. But with all this were mingled an acute sensitivity, an almost shy gentleness, a wide and refined culture in two languages, a love of poetry and a passion for music. The big-game hunter was a great pianist. The man of action, decision and furious energy held an unassuaged dream in his eyes and his voice sometimes quivered with a curious spiritual nostalgia.

Our meetings were very irregular. Conus would suddenly appear in London. The next day, without warning, he would have gone and no one knew where. Once or twice I asked him to what corps or service he belonged. He replied evasively. At that time, many members of the Free French in England replied thus. I did not insist.

And then Conus disappeared for good. And I thought—without the least proof, but with absolute conviction—that he was in France doing some secret, dangerous work.

But I was soon appointed myself to a squadron for special missions and thought no more about him.

A few weeks after the liberation of Paris, I met Boislambert there. He gave me news of our friends.

Bissagnet, who had escaped with him, had been killed in the 1st French Armoured Division.

Médéric, one of the best leaders of the Resistance, had swallowed cyanide to escape the Gestapo.

Bourgoin had immensely distinguished himself.

'And Conus?' I asked.

'He came to see me in my office a few days ago,' Boislambert said. 'He told me his story of the Vercors in detail. As I already knew the outline, I got my secretary to take it down. She did so word for word. I'll send you a copy.'

Boislambert said nothing more. But his voice and expression gave me the feeling that here was an exceptional adventure. But I was far from imagining how exceptional it was.

During the summer of 1944, a British aircraft used for secret work landed Conus in France. And he went to the Vercors massif, where the rugged mountains sheltered an important maquis.

Then, on 21 July, at dawn, German troops attacked from all sides. Their superiority in numbers and weapons was crushing. Without help, the maquisards could expect only a battle of despair. They could do nothing but kill the largest possible number of the enemy before being destroyed themselves. Their commander sent Conus through the German lines to ask for reinforcements.

Accompanied by two young lieutenants, of whom one was the Oisan liaison officer, he left Saint-Martin-du-Vercors during the afternoon of 21 July in the direction of Carençon.

Their first attempt to break through the surrounding enemy was at Pas de la Sambre. An officer called Goderville acted as their guide in this sector. He was really the writer Jean Prévost.

It was raining in torrents. Through the downpour they saw that the FFI advance posts had been evacuated. A German patrol opened fire on them with machine-guns. Conus and his companions were forced to retreat.

Jean Prévost then went to find ten men, two of whom were guides. They were to try to pass the maquisards through the Pas de l'Ane. Jean Prévost then left them to go back to his post. He was killed the next morning.

It was still raining as hard as ever when the little party reached the Pas de l'Ane. They were suddenly stopped by an explosion. The leading guide had been blown up by a mine. The other was ordered to take the wounded man back to the camp.

Night had fallen but it was still raining. Soaked to the skin, the file of hunted men groped their way through the mountains, searching the dark downpour for a pass or negotiable descent. Their blind quest had no success.

In the middle of the night they chanced on a woodcutter's hut, and took refuge in it. There was so little space that the seven soaking, harassed men could not even lie down but had to sit crowded together.

They started off again before dawn. This time, they had the woodcutters from the hut as guides. In thick, blinding mist, they started down a chimney the woodcutters thought practicable. But it proved not to be so without a rope. They had to seek elsewhere.

A few kilometres farther on the guides found another way down, which seemed negotiable. Conus and his companions started down it.

At the beginning, the usual path passed by the Pas de la Balme. This was held by an FFI post. But long before they reached it they heard machine-gun fire coming from its direction. By difficult paths, they made a detour round the post and avoided it. The noise of firing gradually died away. The Germans had destroyed the post.

At last they had passed through the ring of fire and iron encircling the Vercors. The fugitives might have hoped to reach Château-Bernard, a nearby village with safe hiding, without further obstacle. But every village in the whole countryside was full of German troops on the alert; and the police were carefully checking the inhabitants. The maquisards therefore buried their weapons. Conus even threw away the cyanide pill, which all the Resistance fighters from England carried, so that they might choose between torture and suicide if they were captured.

Having taken these precautions, they entered Château-Bernard.

Their first concern was to tidy themselves up so as not to attract attention. Bearded, dirty and soaking wet, they looked like escaped convicts. A friendly farm on the outskirts of the village took them in. They washed, shaved and dried their clothes. Conus was now ready to continue his mission.

To leave Château-Bernard, they had to pass a German roadblock in the Rue Saint-Guillaume. The maquisards presented themselves with their false papers in their hands. The officer in command of the road-block did not even look at the papers; he had orders to hand all strangers over to the German police. This meant a strict interrogation and a detailed search. And Conus had micro-films of codes and figures on him. He had also 200,000 francs in his bag.

The police showed extreme violence from the first. The Allies' successful landing and advance, and the Vercors insurrection nearby, tended to increase their accustomed brutality.

However, before being handed over to the agents of the Gestapo, Conus succeeded in taking the micro-films from his pocket and concealing them between his thumb and forefinger. While the search lasted—and it was long and detailed—he was made to hold his hands against a wall. The micro-films were not discovered.

But Conus had no illusions. There would be enough indications of who they were found on himself, his companions or their belongings to be fatal to them. The game was up. He bitterly regretted having parted with the brown pill that gave supreme freedom.

Indeed, the interrogation soon became almost a massacre. The German police threw themselves on Conus with such brutality that, in spite of his strength and athlete's resistance, he collapsed under their blows. When he fell, they began pounding him ruthlessly with their boots, revolver-butts and batons. Throughout the savage hammering, his one thought was to cover and conceal the micro-films.

The police, having failed to extract any information from their victims, put them in a van. There were already three young men from the maquis in it.

As they were getting into the vehicle, Conus found himself next to the Oisan liaison officer. He whispered to him: 'Let's take a chance and seize the escort's weapons.'

'I can't,' muttered the lieutenant. 'I live here. They know my real name. My family would pay for it.'

The door of the van shut on the prisoners.

They were taken to Vif. There they were interrogated again, even more barbarously. Conus was the one who suffered most. His companions, by involuntary, unconscious gestures, had shown him deference. The packets of bank-notes found in his bag had consecutive numbers. That was enough to prove he was the leader.

The first question they asked him showed this well enough.

'Have you been sent from Algiers or London?'

They dislocated his shoulders with leather thongs. They crushed the ends of his fingers with batons. They held lighted matches to his eyes and threatened to burn them out.

The torture went on—in vain—from two o'clock in the afternoon till nine at night.

Then, tottering, bloody, broken and disfigured, the maquisards were pushed, indeed thrown on top of one another, into a truck which immediately drove off. After some fifteen kilometres they were made to get out near the village of Saint-Barthélemy, opposite a disused lime kiln.

The Germans had told them nothing, but they heard the rattle of weapons behind them and knew that they had reached the end of the road. The believers—among whom were the liaison officer and Conus—said a brief prayer. The others awaited the end in silence.

However, the place selected for the execution was not where the truck had stopped. The condemned had to walk 500 yards along a ravine through which flowed a stream.

I have transcribed Conus' feelings during his walk to execution from the account he gave Boislambert and which, unknown to him, was taken down word for word. I seem to hear his calm, low voice.

'At that moment,' Conus told his friend, 'I was completely resigned to dying. I could not move my arms. I merely felt a certain curiosity.

'We were made to sit down in a field above the ravine. We were surrounded by a guard of six men with pistols, sub-machine guns and rifles at the ready. The nine others went farther up to have a look at the ground. The German warrant officer shouted: "Send them along two by two!"

'Four men came down, selected a lieutenant and a young man from the maquis and made them go twenty yards above us. They made them kneel down and killed them with pistol, sub-machine gun and rifle fire.

'At that moment, I began to hear the stream in the ravine. The sound of it broke the resignation in which I was sunk. I decided to attempt something before dying.'

Yes, I seem to hear Conus' voice. I am sure that, in telling his story, it appeared quite natural to him that the sound of rushing water should have renewed the desire to live in a heart already prepared for death.

At once, all Conus' instincts, as a hunter, tracker, athlete and soldier, were ready to do his behest. One quick, all-embracing glance was enough for him to gauge distances and size up the situation in the evening light of the long summer's day, the shape of the terrain and the positions and behaviour of the guards.

On his left, a Feldwebel was holding his P38 pistol uncocked and in a totally incorrect manner, Conus judged. On his right, there were two soldiers armed with sub-machine guns which he recognised as Schmeissers. A little farther off, there were two more guards, also armed with sub-machine guns.

Finally, in front of him, between himself and the steep slope down to the bed of the stream below, was a man with a Mauser rifle.

And, from his high cheekbones and narrow-lidded eyes, Conus, in one of those moments of peculiarly lucid intuition, felt sure that the man was one of those Russian deserters whom the Germans incorporated in their punitive detachments. And he saw that the Russian was staring fixedly and with a strange reverence at a point in his blood-stained chest which was bare owing to his ragged clothing. And he realised that this grave attention was directed at the cross hanging from his neck. It occurred to him that this Mongol-faced guard was profoundly and superstitiously religious.

However the executions were continuing.

The warrant officer in charge shouted: 'Next!'

The Feldwebel superintending the group of men to be shot then cried: 'March!'

He then waved his pistol negligently to order the nearest two men to get up and walk the twenty yards to the death-place.

Together with the other details, this had also been noted by Conus whose mind, senses and muscles were tensed to the uttermost. Before he knew it himself, his decision had been taken and his plan made.

There was a burst of fire and two maquisards fell dead.

'Next!' cried the warrant officer.

'March!' shouted the Feldwebel.

The Oisan liaison officer and his neighbour got to their feet. They walked a few paces and Conus saw them shot.

It was now his turn. To those of his companions who remained he said a hasty farewell as if he were resigned to his end. But to the last, a boy of seventeen, he could not help whispering, as he shook his hand: 'Watch out and good luck.'

Then Conus heard the metallic voice shouting once again: 'Next!'

And the other replying: 'March!'

He gave the Feldwebel's pistol a furtive glance. As he had expected, the weapon was waved vaguely in his direction to indicate that he should climb the slope. This was the signal he was waiting for.

He got slowly to his feet, his body tensely gathered like a coiled spring. And at the moment it uncoiled, he fixed his eyes with all his will to live on those of the deserter from the Red Army, who was barring his way to the ravine, and shouted *in Russian*: 'As you believe in God, don't fire!'

And Conus who, three minutes before, had been exhausted, weak and despairing, took off like a hundred yards runner, and made straight for the Russian. And the Russian, instead of firing, stood aside and let the condemned man pass...

On reading this passage in Conus' account, I remembered my astonishment when, without warning, he had suddenly addressed me in Russian in the American bomber. And I could easily imagine the sort of sacred shock that must have petrified the devout peasant from the Volga, the Urals or Siberia, whom the chances of war and servitude had brought to these French hills, when he suddenly heard this appeal to his faith in his native tongue.

But the other guards and executioners had no similar reasons for sparing Conus. As he dashed forward, he saw in the gathering twilight the flash of the negligent Feldwebel's pistol. Then all the submachine guns came into action. There was a crackling of dozens of shots.

But the effect of surprise impaired their aim as did the speed with which Conus moved. He was already on the edge of the ravine. He gathered himself together and jumped as far out as he could. He landed some thirty feet down.[1]

His luck held and his fall was broken by a large hazel bush. He tumbled out of the tree and dashed down the slope. The Germans kept up a continuous fire from above. He was not hit. But when he reached the bottom of the ravine, he had to halt to recover his breath.

He took advantage of this necessary respite to have a quick look at the terrain. The slope beyond the stream was bare and without a single tree. There was no shelter there.

Conus therefore fled along the ravine on the same bank. He

[1] He was later able to measure the distance himself.

soon came to an area covered thickly by brambles. He dived into them and lay flat, dug into the mud and covered himself with dead leaves. It was time. His pursuers had reached the bottom of the slope.

And here, from the shorthand account, is the end of Conus' story:

'The brambles covered an area of some ten by two hundred yards. The Germans beat it yard by yard, searching the thickets with sticks and bayonets. The Feldwebel came to a halt with his boots a yard from my head. I saw the brambles move above my head. I heard the Germans discussing the situation. One said he was sure he had wounded me. The others were promising me a peculiarly unpleasant death.

'Then the beaters moved past me. I could hear my heart beating against my ribs. I was completely exhausted. I could scarcely move my arms.

'Ten minutes later, the Germans came back and searched the thicket again, even more carefully. But the brambles and the mud with which I had covered myself saved me.

'The Germans held a council of war ten yards from me. I heard them mention the word *hunde* (dog) and I realised I would have to be quick.

'I heard a German go down to the road and a car start. It was now night. I began to disengage myself from the brambles and the mud. I slipped into the stream. I could see two German sentries on the other side, about thirty yards apart.

'I crawled between them and climbed up the same side of the ravine by which I had come down. I passed within five yards of my companions' bodies. I crawled into a cornfield. Then I followed a stream which took me to the road. I rolled across the road, fell into a field and reached the Gresse. I went into the stream and followed the Gresse for five hundred yards. At this moment, I was strongly tempted to give up and seek refuge in a farm I knew five kilometres away.

'Then, having thought it over, I continued on my way, taking my direction from the stars: East South-East.

'I walked all night, sometimes falling asleep from sheer fatigue. When the cold woke me, I went on again. At two o'clock the next afternoon, I arrived within sight of the Drac valley where I knew ı a German town full of troops and Gestapo. It seemed quite . to him.

mission was to gather information,' he went on in the same onversational tone. 'But where were you to get it in a terror-n town which was being continuously bombed by the British, ıericans and the French? The streets were nothing but ruins, e population thought of nothing but taking cover. It was not good nosing about in that.'

had reached a café.

lrink will do us good,' Conus said.

ɜn our drinks came, he went on: 'In fact, it was the panic and er that gave me my chance. One day, as the wounded, the ted and the dead were being brought out from a totally des- working-class district, I heard some women mutter: "The et away with it all right. With those luxurious six-storey ground shelters of theirs, lifts and all, they don't have to ."

e word lift was like a sudden flash of light. That very evening, ; a lull in the raids, I assembled some of my men in front of a which housed the headquarters of one of the big Ruhr trusts. illed the caretaker and the liftman, whom we found in a ificent basement, and took their uniforms. Two of our men sed themselves and the rest of us went down. There really six storeys of concrete below ground. The bottom one was, of e, the safest and the best fitted up. We didn't have to wait long. night the bombers really surpassed themselves. The lift-bell continuously. It was merely a question of going up and collect-ıe customers.'

nus burst out laughing.

ıd what customers!' he went on. 'High officials, big indus-ts, chiefs of police, generals. That cellar, secure from bombs, ortably upholstered and carefully furnished, provided with and drink, was their club, their safety club. We tied them up nterrogated them one after the other. And we got information ght that night, and good information at that.'

e had finished our drinks.

nd now?' I asked. 'Now that there's no more war.'

m going to see what's happening at home, in Africa,' Conus

the bridge was guarded by the Germans. I sa field and took the risk of accosting her. Whe gan to weep and said: "My poor Monsieur, h and fetch Monsieur le Curé."

'The priest took me to a farm. They fed came to fetch me and help me cross the D took me to the Chief of the Isère FFI to w sage. I had preserved the micro-films. I was codes and send a first appeal to London for the Isère units who were to make a di Vercors.'

When I had read this account, and had emotions it aroused, I telephoned Boislambe

'Yes,' he said. 'We both know a good man the Resistance. But none like this.'

'What about Conus?' I asked. 'How is he?

'Fighting fit,' Boislambert said.

'Where is he?'

'In the Ruhr,' Boislambert said. 'That's al

At that time, the Allies were still on the l

Hitler had committed suicide and the Ger unconditionally. I ran into Conus on the walked a little way together.

He was as broad-shouldered and vigorous-

I said: 'You're looking very well for executed!'

He made a face and replied: 'Forget it. I sides, to have been a game-animal oneself for pleasant memory.'

He laughed and added: 'However, at Dus satisfying bag to add to my game-book.'

'When was that?' I asked.

'Before the crossing of the Rhine,' Conus s

'Then you mean in enemy territory?'

'Oh, in plain clothes and with a good tea Conus said.

He did not bother to explain how he had

His eyes suddenly grew bright.

'I'm going to try out some sporting rifles I picked up in Germany. They're superb.'

These and a racing car were his booty.

After his demobilisation, Colonel Bourgoin had been appointed chief game warden to the Ministry of France Over-Seas. The old poacher's job was to see that the regulations concerning elephants and the hides of wild animals, which he had himself disregarded for so long, were properly applied.

'It's rather like the story of Vidocq,' he said. 'The outlaw becomes chief of police.'

One day, I told him of my last conversation with Conus.

'He's not in Africa at all,' Bourgoin said. 'It was suggested he should do a tour of duty in Indo-China. He jumped at it.'

Bourgoin glanced for a second at his empty right sleeve—regret, resignation?—and went on: 'He's a colonel now. He's got a commando unit which he has built up man by man. He'll make the sparks fly all right.'

Months went by. From time to time I heard Conus' name mentioned by people returning from the Far East. His unit was famous for the lightning speed with which it moved, its furious courage in battle, its inexhaustible resistance to physical hardship and its pitiless severity in repression.

And then I heard from Conus. He was in Paris and invited me to dine.

Our meeting was as always friendly, pleasant and gay. Yet his voice seemed more subdued, more veiled, than usual. There seemed to me to be also a strange weariness in his eyes.

'When are you going back to Indo-China?' I asked him.

'Never,' Conus said. 'It seems I've picked up some mysterious disease out there. No one seems to know whether it's a microbe, a virus or a parasite. I shall become an habitué of Val-de-Grâce.'

'And that's why . . .'

I did not complete my question, but he understood and said: 'You're quite right, that's not why I've given up.'

He toyed a moment with his empty glass, and then looked at me, his eyes full of a quiet, sad weariness.

'I've had enough of killing people,' he said. 'I've been doing nothing else for the last five years. In Africa, in France, in Germany and in the rice fields. Killing all the time!'

He smiled, but only with the corners of his mouth.

'Oh, I'm an expert! I've had the best tuition. In England, at the secret missions' school, the most famous surgeons showed us how to go neatly for the heart and cut a cardial artery in the proper manner . . . I went into it wholeheartedly. There are people who haven't any idea how to make war. . .'

He played with his glass again, looked away, and went on: 'Only it's like this . . . You take a Vietnam village whose inhabitants have been accomplices to an ambush in which some of your comrades have been killed. All right, no one will talk. So you line up the inhabitants and you shoot one in ten. It's the usual dose. All right. And as you put your pistol to the back of his head, the chap—a peasant, an artisan, a student—cries from his heart: "Long live liberty!" or: "I don't mind dying, there are others." And then another village, and another. And always killing. So I let them have their way with me about Val-de-Grâce.'

However, he did not let them have their way with him for long. He left for Africa.

And this is what I heard.

Conus took his plantation in hand again. Then organised an enormous safari.

While hunting, did he think with a tender smile of Bourgoin, his old friend and accomplice, whose duty it now was to enforce the laws he was in process of breaking so lightheartedly, armed with the German rifles which were part of his wartime booty?

Whether stalking or driving, the safari was a triumph. To celebrate it, Conus, on his return, invited his numerous friends in the district to dinner. Towards the end of the meal, Conus got to his feet, squared his athletic shoulders, and picked up a glass of champagne. He raised it to his lips and fell dead.

Thus died the man who had given back its song to a stream in the mountains of the Vercors.

17
THE ZOMBIE

TO REACH Afghanistan, the eternal crossroads where the great Mongol steppe meets the gigantic wall of the Hindu Kush, the aircraft has the whole compass card at its disposal.

It can come from Persia in the West or India in the East, from Pakistan in the South or Russia in the North. But whatever line you take—Iranian or Indian Airlines, Dutch KLM or Russian Aeroflot—it is a little two-engined plane which crosses the pitiless deserts and wild mountain ranges to deposit its passengers on the immediate outskirts of Kabul.

This is necessitated by the lie of the land at an altitude of over 5,000 feet, and the condition of the runways. All around, an almost perfect circle of peaks and burnt mountains supports the sky like a huge serrated shell.

The swarming Indian cities of Bombay and Calcutta are much farther from Europe than Kabul. And farther again are Rangoon, Bangkok, Hong Kong and Tokyo. But in these the link of the airlines, the architecture of the airfield buildings, the routines and formalities are all similar to those at the point of departure. And the frequency of the air transports, wearing the signs of all the great airline companies of the world, assure constant, rapid and certain liaison with it.

But on the airfield that serves the Afghan capital, the smallness of the aircraft, the cloud of dust it raises from the parched, cracked ground, the singular shape of the buildings, the circle of arid peaks closing the horizon and behind which one divines the outline of colossal mountains, all suddenly give one a feeling of having come to the end of the world.

Three travellers from France, who landed in a Dakota at noon on an August day, welcomed this sensation of isolation and remoteness with intense excitement.

One of them, aged thirty-five, with blue eyes and a fair beard trimmed to a point, was called Jacques Dupont. The second, who was much younger, very slender of body, thin-faced and with narrow-lidded eyes, was called Pierre Schoendoerffer. I was the third.

The adventure had begun. And for me it was also the start of an entirely new undertaking. I was not merely to investigate this unknown, difficult country, but also to make a film.

I had often wished, when at the sources of the Nile, in darkest Africa, or in the ruby mines at Mogok in Burma, or in the junk-covered bay at Hong Kong, and aware of the powerlessness of the written word to paint the miracles of nature and the strange colours of men's lives, that I had with me cameramen who could record the splendour of peoples and places.

A producer had heard my regrets. And, since I was to write about Afghanistan for *France-Soir*, he had formed a little team of technicians to accompany me there.

The advance party had now landed at Kabul.

The summer sun of Central Asia was at its zenith. It burnt our skins through our thin clothes. The light was a sort of sharp, dazzling powder that hurt our eyes in spite of our dark glasses. But, after the days we had had to spend in New Delhi, where the damp, overheated air seemed to be made of clammy embers, so that it was almost impossible to breathe, while the dark, ashen clouds of the monsoon made of the sky and the city a sort of sweat-room, the dryness and luminosity of the high Afghan plateau was welcome.

Besides, my two companions were long accustomed to hot climates. Dupont had made several documentaries in Equatorial Africa. As for Schoendoerffer, from love of his profession and of taking risks, he had dropped by parachute with his camera at Dien-Bien-Phu when disaster was already imminent. He had shared the agonies of the fortress and the captivity of the survivors.

By nature and profession, they were intrepid, had the wanderlust, and were more sensitive than most men to the violence of certain landscapes and the hues of those bare expanses that bear the seal of the eternal.

And indeed, since leaving India, the flight had provided us with many riches of this sort. After Amritsar, with its golden palaces and temples amid still waters, we had flown among inhuman splendours, following their spell-like windings.

For the Dakota was unable to fly over the mountains and had to make its way between their flanks, through valleys, gorges and defiles. The passes were often so narrow that the aircraft's line of flight sometimes appeared to be following the shape of the great rocks. The pilot would raise now one wing, now the other to avoid a crash. If either engine failed there could be no escape for the aircraft among these gigantic hazards. But their beauty aroused more excitement than fear. Ochre, brown, buff and sienna, the frieze of peaks and summits was constantly developing, outlined to infinity against a splendid sky. All was immutable and yet ever-changing in this sublime aridity. Craters of harsh shadow, pale arenas, austere mountain-sides, shining peaks—it was a burning, flamboyant desert on the march, boiling with high mineral waves. Its august, barren hardness was the earth's primitive shell. And we were so close to it that it seemed as if we could touch its pitiless, venerable grain.

Then, in the hollows of the valleys as they gradually grew wider, appeared bare, rough, lustreless, powdery patches of green. On their edges stood tiny cubes of dried mud, houses without shelter either from the sun or the fierce winds. It was impossible to believe that human families lived in these strange hamlets on a dead planet. And yet, on the tracks like thin pale ribbons that linked them, one could see from time to time the winding caterpillars of caravans.

With our faces to the little square windows of the Dakota, we watched the barriers of the world rise and fall. It was the Afghanistan of our dreams all right, closed, wild, bristling with inaccessible mountains, and inhabited by tribes born to war and freedom. It was the Afghanistan we had come to film.

The aircraft's engines hummed steadily on. Its movement was gentle and peaceful. In the cabin, which contained very few passengers, there was the wonderful freshness of the mountains in summer. From our flying carpet everything seemed so simple and easy...

In reality, however, nothing could have been more hazardous and difficult than our enterprise.

We none of us knew anything of the country beyond what we had gathered from conversations and books. We knew nothing of the language, customs, prices, means of transport, state of the roads or accessible districts.

And, before winter closed in and made travel impossible, we had only three months—perhaps four—in which to make our film. It was a race against time, a gamble against days and hours.

But we all three liked games of chance. And now, our heads still full of the splendid landscapes, we gaily entered the line of one-storeyed, whitewashed buildings, roofed in corrugated iron, which housed the administrative services of the Kabul airfield.

We imagined that, for the moment at least, there would be no difficulties. The day before, at New Delhi, the French Embassy in India had cabled the French Embassy in Afghanistan asking them to meet us at the airfield. As for accommodation, we had reserved it by telegram from Paris at the Grand Hotel.

There were Russians meeting a charming young Russian couple who had travelled with us; there were Americans meeting a senior official from the United States; and there were Indians greeting with bright eyes and flashing teeth their fellow-countryman off the 'plane; but there was no one to meet us.

The porters had long ago put our luggage into the Customs hall and we were still waiting, near the little car park, for a messenger from the Embassy to take us to the unknown town. The Americans departed in a Chevrolet; the Russians in a Pobieda; the Indians in a Jeep . . . No one remained but people attached to the airfield: rather ragged workmen, soldiers and Customs officers in faded uniforms, officials dressed in European clothes but wearing, despite the heat, long, narrow Astrakhan hats. It was becoming clear that we were being left to our own resources.

The agent of the Indian Airlines showed us his company's bus: an ageless, nameless, colourless and almost shapeless truck, its sides dented, its glass broken, an incredible wreck abandoned to the devouring sun. It was due to go to Kabul, when all the administrative details concerning the freight had been concluded.

It was getting hotter and hotter. The agent of the Indian Airlines advised us to await the truck's departure in a little building where tea was served.

A waiter, dressed in a flowing shirt and wide trousers, who limped on one crooked leg, brought us the tea. We scarcely spoke.

The suffocating days in New Delhi, the sleepless nights, the start at dawn, the constant nervous tension, and the effect of the sun and the altitude were beginning to tell on us.

The noise of attempts to start a recalcitrant engine with a starting-handle drew us from our semi-coma. The truck was trembling, quivering, vibrating and grinding in every joint. The prospect of driving into Kabul in such a vehicle amused us. It was like a film adventure.

The short road from the airfield to the town was wide, smooth and tarred. Hills and peaks stood out against the azure of the sky on every horizon. We passed people with strange faces and curious clothes, files of little donkeys, and friezes of heavily laden camels. And, at the end of the journey, there awaited us a good lodging in the Grand Hotel, with a shower and exotic foods.

We passed through a district of spacious streets lined with high mud walls. Through the doorways we could see gardens. There were often soldiers on guard—ministries and embassies, no doubt. Suddenly the truck turned into a crowded, tumultuous street, full of shops and booths, and came to a halt. The Indian driver invited us to get out. He spoke in English.

'But we're going to the Grand Hotel,' I said.

'This is it,' he replied.

He pointed to a few steps, worn with use, that led to a low, narrow door, which was flanked by a barber's shop. Above, on a wooden placard, was written in faded letters: Hotel Kabul.

'This is the Grand Hotel?' I asked hesitantly.

'There is no other,' the driver replied.

Dark-faced servants were already hurrying down the steps and seizing our luggage, while a curious thin-faced crowd in flowing garments and turbans of every shape and size was gathering round us.

The hall of the hotel was an ante-chamber furnished with a table and tired-looking chairs. Then there was a dark, stiflingly hot lounge. Near the door, behind a desk on which a small fan turned in vain, sprawled a fat, bald man in shirt-sleeves. He was dripping with perspiration. He got up, saluted us and said, as he looked us over with bright, gentle eyes: 'I am happy to welcome you. My name is Ali Wali.'

His manners were refined. He spoke admirable French in a

hoarse, weary voice. I complimented him on the fact. He replied with nonchalant melancholy: 'I have lived a lot in Paris, in the good old days, when Montmartre was at its best . . . the Rat Mort, L'Abbaye de Thélème. . .'

I asked him to show us our rooms.

'There are no rooms,' he said.

My companions and I simultaneously wiped the sticky sweat from our faces. Though the hotel had seemed so wretched, how desirable it appeared to us now.

'But what about our telegram?' said Jacques Dupont, nervously pulling at the point of his blond beard.

'I don't know whether the management received it,' Ali Wali replied kindly and regretfully. 'But the hotel is full and there is a waiting-list of at least fifty people. You see, it will soon be the Jachem Istiqual, the Festival of Independence.'

'We know that,' I cried. 'It's because of that we reserved rooms.'

Ali Wali looked at us with his light, kind, friendly eyes, then bent his bald, sweaty forehead over his fan and repeated: 'Fifty people on the waiting-list . . . the Jachem. . .'

We left him to go to the French Embassy, and even forgot to ask the way.

As we were going rather disappointedly down the steps, Schoendoerffer gave a shout. A little French car was parked some distance to our right. It obviously belonged to a fellow-countryman and doubtless to a member of the Embassy staff. It began to move off. Jacques Dupont, who is a good runner, dashed after it, caught up with it, and cried: 'Monsieur! Monsieur!'

The car stopped and the face of a young man, with very dark hair, calm, mocking eyes, and a little moustache over an ironical mouth, appeared at the window.

'What can I do for you?' he asked.

Like the interpreter of the Hotel Kabul, he had a soft, weary voice. He, too, was dressed in European clothes, spoke perfect French, but was not a Frenchman.

'Afghan, pure Afghan,' he said with a dazzling smile. 'My name's Rahim Sadozin, but I am entirely at your service.'

He drove us to the French Embassy and promised to find us a house, which was no easy task because of the approaching festival.

By the time he dropped us in a street lined, like so many, with high, whitewashed mud walls, in front of a porch flanked by a sentry-box, in which a soldier stood on guard, and surmounted by the tricolour, we had a friend in Kabul. He dealt in astrakhan furs and ran a trucking company called, simply, Pamir Transport.

M. Brière, the French ambassador to Afghanistan, intelligent, elegant, well-informed and extremely courteous, welcomed us with the best grace in the world. And it was kind of him, for not only had he not received the telegram from New Delhi informing him of our arrival, but he was already putting up four French geographers who had had a misadventure similar to ours at the Hotel Kabul two days before.

'The house is full and I regret having no beds for you,' M. Brière said. 'But we'll find something. Let's have luncheon first.'

At luncheon, besides our team and the geographers, robust young men with thick hair, who had come by the Karachi route, there was another Frenchman. He was a man of some fifty years of age, tall, slender and sunburnt, and had a somewhat arched nose, energetic features and fine, thoughtful brown eyes that had a touch of gold about them. After luncheon, he took the ambassador aside and talked to him in a low voice. When the conversation was over, the ambassador said: 'I think we've found a solution. M. Hinstin, who is the representative of Air France here, has recently become president of the Kabul French club. He proposes to put you up there until something better turns up.'

We were given two rooms which were used as cloakrooms. *Charpois* (wooden frames joined with webbing and mattresses stuffed with cotton) were produced. Such was our first lodging in Kabul.

We went to the centre of the town in a *gadi.* I sat in front with the driver. My companions sat with their backs to us on the rear seat. The hot sun made the trap's bumping wheels and the horse's green plume shine.

Everything was still new to me, and excited my interest.

Our driver had a large turban and a light whip. I tried to converse with him by gestures. Though he did not understand, he invariably answered: '*Balé*' (which means: very good). And burst out laughing. Like all the Afghan lower classes, he was polite and good-humoured in spite of a poor, hard life.

He dropped us in the most frequented street at a photographer's shop. Schoendoerffer and Dupont required photographs for the residence and travel permits we needed. Since I already had some, I told my friends I would meet them at the Hotel Kabul opposite.

For a few minutes I lost myself happily in the crowd, with its noise and its colours. Long, wide tunics, the striped *chapanes* from the north, European clothes, Astrakhan hats, the *chadris* of the women, street-porters in rags, the pale blue pyjamas of the *Lazaras*, the street-cleaners. . .

In the street, the cars sounding horns mingled with the joyous bells of the *gadis*. But it was neither the smartest nor most comfortable (Chevrolets for the most part) that attracted my attention. I gazed hungrily at the American and Russian Jeeps, the only vehicles which, outside Kabul and a few stretches of special road, could travel across Afghanistan. All those I saw belonged to public services, embassies, missions and a few rich individuals. But it was impossible to find one either to hire or buy. Every attempt we had made had been in vain. And I began thinking once again of the idea that obsessed my companions and myself: how were we to organise transport? For, without transport, there would be no film.

I climbed the worn steps of the Hotel Kabul to await my friends inside.

In the sort of narrow ante-chamber, which was in half-darkness and furnished with a table and a few old chairs, only one chair was occupied. On seeing me, the man sitting in it made two almost simultaneous but opposite movements. He got quickly to his feet, as if he had been waiting for me, and then, realising his mistake, sat down again with a groan.

He was a European of about thirty years of age, short and thick-set, with a worn face, hollowed by anxiety and fatigue, and a freckled forehead to which a precocious baldness lent height. He wore a crumpled and stained tweed coat, and an open-necked khaki shirt. He was very hot and in a very bad temper.

I chose the chair farthest from his.

Almost immediately two Afghans came in. One was very young, very handsome and was wearing a grey Astrakhan hat. He was probably a student. The other was middle-aged, very tall and broad-shouldered, and was wearing wide trousers, a long brown mackintosh and a majestic turban. His broad face sported a fan-shaped hennaed beard. He was undoubtedly a rich merchant.

The man in the crumpled tweed coat jumped up, scarcely greeted the new arrivals and said in English to the young Afghan, who was serving as interpreter: 'Well, has he made up his mind?'

The boy replied with some embarrassment: 'He wants to think it over and make further inquiries about prices.'

The man's face assumed an expression of impatience and anger, which showed up the strong line of his jaw beneath the freckled cheeks.

'I must have an answer before noon tomorrow,' he said. 'Tell him so.'

When he had listened to the translation, the merchant slowly stroked his big red beard, smiled and spoke. He had magnificent teeth.

'What's he saying?' the Englishman asked furiously.

'He says that in Kandahar, where he comes from, thought is considered a virtue.'

The two Afghans went off. The man in the tweed coat opened the neck of his khaki shirt still wider and fell back into his chair, which groaned under him. He wiped his sweaty face on his sleeve and, in a low but clear voice, gave vent to a number of the crudest oaths in the English language. His expression was no longer one of fury but of despair. I could not help looking at him with a certain curiosity. Our eyes met.

'Are you having a bit of trouble?' I asked him in spite of myself.

This indiscretion, far from annoying him, seemed to give him the greatest pleasure. He needed a confidant. He cried: 'A bit of trouble! It's hell! That's the word for it. Hell!'

Then he told me his story.

He was called Dave. He was Irish by birth, but lived in London where he was an engineer. A few months before, he had married a young English girl, who designed for the stage. She liked travelling, as he did, and they had determined to spend their honeymoon in going to the south of India by car. From there, they would take ship for Australia for the Olympic games.

They were counting on a car belonging to the wife's uncle. He was a rich man and had promised to lend them his Rolls Royce.

But when the uncle heard of their proposed itinerary, he had withdrawn his offer. Then Dave, whose hard, clear-cut jaw revealed stubbornness, had bought an old army cross-country truck and had had a new engine put into it. However, by the time he had paid for the truck, the engine, new wheels, spare parts and a trailer, he had no money left for the journey itself. Then Dave had had another idea. He published an advertisement offering to take with him for a modest price a few Australians who wanted to go home by an unusual route.

Five or six passengers would have been enough. More than fifty applied. Dave accepted the first fifteen, which was as many as his truck could take. He installed benches and a table; and loaded the trailer with tents, tins of food, water-cans and medical supplies. And one fine day, with his wife beside him, he took the wheel and headed east.

They crossed the Channel by the ferry. They drove happily and without difficulty through Europe. But then...

Dave hid his bald forehead behind his nervous, spatulate fingers.

'Turkey... Irak... Iran... Afghanistan...' he groaned. 'The roads! The quagmires! Hills like staircases! Bridges carried away by rivers in spate! Fords through which the bogged truck had to be hauled.'

Dave clenched his fists and his jaw.

'The truck held out all right,' he said proudly. 'But the Australians... Never mention Australians to me again. They're quick-tempered and undisciplined. They'd drink any water, even though we'd made a compact always to disinfect it. Two of them nearly died. We had to wait till they recovered. Then the heat and the flies. The others lost their tempers, quarrelled among themselves, and held my wife and me responsible for everything. We had words—and it nearly came to blows.'

In short, on arriving in Kabul, the passengers had refused to continue the journey with Dave, had taken air-tickets for Ceylon and had left without paying him. To put the lid on things, his wife had fallen ill with nervous exhaustion and dysentery. She was in the British Embassy hospital. They had no money left at all, and their transit visas, which had already been renewed, were again on the point of expiring. Dave had only one resource left: to sell his truck.

But Customs duties and taxes doubled its price for an Afghan.

'And there it is!' said Dave. 'To hell with the whole business!'

Once again he wiped his forehead and neck on his sleeve. But for me, in that dark, damp ante-chamber, with its smell of mutton fat from the kitchen, the man's harassed, emaciated, sweaty face seemed to be that of luck itself. We were in despair of finding transport. And this man had a sound truck, which indeed had given proof of its soundness, since it had brought seventeen people and their luggage all the way from France over impossible roads.

'Would foreigners,' I asked Dave, 'have to pay Customs dues?'

'Of course not,' he said in surprise. 'Why?'

At this point, my two friends arrived, delighted with their visit to the photographer. They had met three Afghan girls in his studio. They had unveiled in their presence without hesitation. They were beautiful. They had smiled at them. Faces, when suddenly unveiled, seem to take on an extra quality...

I introduced my friends to Dave and told them of our conversation. Their eyes gleamed. They, too, saw the miracle developing.

'We would like to see your truck,' I said.

It was now Dave's eyes that expressed a sense of the miraculous.

There were, however, some major obstacles to the negotiations. In the first place we were no mechanics, and could not blindly risk several hundred thousand francs.

Then a second miracle took place.

As we were leaving the Hotel Kabul, two huge Swiss came in. One wore a beard trimmed in the Yankee manner, with the upper lip shaven. He looked like Abraham Lincoln and was a journalist. The other was a watch manufacturer. They had come from Geneva without any trouble at all in a simple 2 hp Citroen. It belonged to the watch manufacturer. And he was one of those men who seem to be born to take engines to pieces and put them together again, to live among the secrets of their mechanisms. We had met them a few days before and immediately lost sight of them, for they had gone off to the south. And now here they were back again just when they were needed.

Dave brought the truck to a steep hill in the neighbourhood of Kabul. The watch manufacturer, who was to vet it as a mechanic, tried it out. His verdict was that the truck was sound except for some necessary repairs which he detailed. Dave had told us in advance of the need for them and had promised to get them done in the British Embassy garage which was run by a careful Scotsman.

So, from that point of view, everything was all right. It was now merely a question of doing a deal.

The only trouble was that we had no money.

We had left Paris before the rather lengthy arrangements had been completed for obtaining foreign currency and transferring it. We had therefore arrived in Kabul with just enough money for our personal expenses during the first few days. The bulk of our money was to be brought from New Delhi by the other two members of our team, the film technician Raoul Contard and his assistant Renaud Lambert, who had left France a week after us with all the equipment for making the film.

I told Dave of the situation when he had brought us back to the Hotel Kabul and I was alone with him. At first he did not seem to understand. His eyes moved from the truck he had thought sold, to the crowd in the street, among which he suddenly seemed lost and abandoned. Then he swore loudly and said in a flat voice: 'I can't wait. My visa's expiring and I've got debts. I shall have to accept the conditions of the merchant with the red beard.'

What could I do?

At that moment the last miracle occurred. Charles Hinstin came up to us. Some fifty years of age, he was tall and elegant and had a fine, firm, sensible face, and eyes the colour of gold, which were always smiling and yet were at the same time melancholy.

He knew Dave and said: 'I've still got some whisky left in my room. Will you both come up?'

Dave sadly shook his head.

'My wife's expecting me at the hospital and I've got to take this darned truck back,' he grumbled.

'Poor devil,' Hinstin said as he watched the truck move off. 'Do you know his story?'

I shrugged and said: 'We've spent all morning with him.'

And as I accompanied Hinstin up to the first floor of the hotel, where he lived, I told him of our disappointed hopes.

'The truck could have been the salvation of both of us,' I concluded as we entered his room.

He turned away to open a cupboard and said casually: 'Well, buy it then!'

'But you don't understand,' I said. 'We haven't got the money.'

Hinstin was rummaging in the cupboard and I could see only his back.

'But I have,' he said. 'I'll lend it to you.'

He turned towards me, holding a bottle and two glasses. I looked at him in astonishment and with the embarrassment an over-generous offer that nothing can justify arouses.

'Really,' I said, 'are you a sorcerer or a Maecenas?'

He turned his golden eyes on me. They were full of laughter and sadness.

'I'm only a *zombie*,' he said.

The whisky had been poured out. The noises of Kabul entered the little room through the open window: the guttural murmur of the crowd, horses' hooves, cries of the donkey-boys, the bells of the galloping *gadis*. Was it the effect of solitude? Or of my curiosity? Or of growing confidence? Hinstin told me the story of his life.

He could and should have been a rich member of the upper-middle class. He seemed destined to be one, owing to his family, and the wealth accumulated by his father, a remarkable engineer and inventor, who had been associated from the start with André Citroen's genius. But Charles Hinstin was not the man to accept destinies arranged at birth.

At twenty, engaged as a workman tanner by an American he had met in the El Garron nightclub, he set sail for the United States. He had known crises, disastrous poker games, unemployment, had become a docker in Chicago, had jumped goods trains, sold cars and finally returned to France in a state-room with a great deal of money.

He spent it all in a few weeks and then set off again, first for Morocco and then for the Cameroons, where he became a development manager, the friend of Glaoni, an engineer-prospector, a planter, the manager of a bar and a hotel, a hunter, the companion of a Vanderbilt, who began his régime of Pernod at seven o'clock in the morning and got drunk three times a day. This life of ups and downs and adventure after adventure had lasted ten years.

After his father's death, Hinstin returned to France to take charge of a factory in the Ardennes. And then the war came.

He was taken prisoner, escaped and joined the secret army. At the beginning of 1943, he was regional chief of all the departments between Clermont-Ferrand and Toulouse. In May, he became national chief of the headquarters of the maquis. In August, ten members of the Gestapo, armed with sub-machine guns, arrested him in a café in Limoges...

At this point in his story, Hinstin stopped to refill our glasses. As the irregular symphony from the Kabul street filled the room. Hinstin gazed for a moment at the whisky, which was much the same colour as his eyes, and smilingly went on: 'It's from that moment that I consider myself a *zombie.* To whom do the negroes give that name? To people who, though dead, are not precisely so and continue to walk the earth. Well, I should have died three times. And yet I'm here with you.

'Death Number One. At Limoges, at the directions of Mayer, a Frenchman, a former lieutenant of Intelligence, who did terrible harm to the Resistance networks, the Gestapo went to work on me. They beat me up and pretended to be about to execute me, but without much result. Mayer told me that I was to be transferred to Lyons by the next convoy and that there I would be for it.

'Three days later, he came into my cell and said: "You're not going to Lyons after all, but to Paris, to Romainville Fort, as a hostage."

'The reason for the change was that a captain of the Deuxième Bureau, who had strangled a German sentry, had been taken from the Limoges prison by the Lyons Gestapo in Mayer's absence and without informing him. To avenge this insolence, Mayer had decided no longer to hand over his prisoners who had been condemned to death to Lyons, but to Romainville. This access of vanity saved my life. At least for the moment.

'Death Number Two. At Romainville I was placed, with two friends who had also come from Limoges, at the top of the list of hostages to be executed. And, on 2nd October—you see I remember the date—they came to fetch fifty men from Romainville to be shot that night as a reprisal for the murder of a chief recruiter for forced labour. The hostages were called out by numbers, according to their order on the list, and were taken to a cell where they made a parcel of their belongings and gave the address to which they were to be sent. Name after name was read out. They reached fifty and still my name and those of my two friends had not been called, though we were at the top of the list.

'We discovered why the next day. Our names were indeed at the top of the list, but since we had only just arrived our papers had not yet reached Romainville. There was nothing about us in the register. The evening the messengers from the Wehrmacht came to collect the hostages, the *sonderführer* of Romainville was in Paris. He knew our dossiers by heart and would not have hesitated to send us to the firing squad. His absence, and his subordinates' fear of taking responsibility, saved my life once again. Temporarily, anyhow.

'Death Number Three. I left with the first convoy for Buchenwald and arrived there in the middle of winter. There were thirty-seven degrees of frost and I had a temperature of 104°.

'I was admitted to the infirmary with a comrade who was in precisely the same state as I was. But the doctor warned us that there was room only for one and that he would keep whichever of us had the highest temperature. We were placed side by side with thermometers under our arms. I happened to be near the stove, and won by the tenth of a degree. The other man died of cold during the night. Had it turned out the other way, his fate would certainly have been mine. I had purulent pleurisy.

'I was saved only because the surgeon, who had also been deported, removed two of my ribs in an emergency operation, though the emergency was somewhat relative. The day after my admission, I was already on the operating table, when I was ordered to get off it and clear out. The operating theatre had been hastily requisitioned by a member of the SS so that his dog, which had broken a leg, could receive proper treatment. My turn was postponed till next day. However, I survived.

'And, what's more, death from exhaustion was only avoided due to the fact that Red Cross parcels (and this was wholly exceptional) were distributed in Buchenwald just at that time.'

Cries of donkey-boys, the plaint of a beggar, an Afghan flute, the bells of the *gadis*. Hinstin was smiling.

The *zombie* continued to walk about the great world.

That is how, thanks to a newly married and adventurous young Irishman, a cargo of angry Australians, a Swiss tourist who manufactured watches and a Frenchman who had survived Buchenwald, our team came by a truck in Kabul.

The colossal range of the Hindu Kush cuts Afghanistan in two. And the contrast between the two slopes is absolute.

To the south, the high valleys (Kabul has an altitude of over 5,000 feet), inhabited by the Pathans and Pushtus, with long aquiline faces, lead to the threshold of India.

To the north of the giant barrier, as far as the Russian frontier, extends an immense steppe inhabited by Mongol tribes. This was where we started shooting.

I shall never forget our journey to and sojourn in these strange lands. Dizzy passes at a height of over 9,000 feet, the grand panoramas of ridges, summits and peaks, precipices bounding the hazardous roads, the wild grandeur of gorges, hidden oases by the rivers like secret paradises, long halts in *chaikhanas* where they served black or green tea, hot *chuppatis* and skewers of mutton, passing nomad caravans led by armed men, while the fiercely beautiful women swayed to the slow pace of the camels, which were dyed with henna and decorated with many coloured plumes.

And suddenly, emerging from the last defile, there was the steppe as far as the eye could reach; and then, in town after town, Tashkungan, Mazar-Y-Sherif, Akcha, the bright, shady, unreal bazaars of Central Asia; and the halts in houses full of precious carpets, where we reclined on deep cushions, among the chiefs and notables dressed in striped silk robes, yellow-gold, emerald green, sienna, wine-coloured. . .

And the generous welcome which had nothing to do with wealth, a royal hospitality from both the richest and the poorest. And the tented camp set up for us on a plateau dominating the limitless steppe on which thousands of Astrakhan sheep with sumptuous coats were herded for us and horsemen, among the best in the world, fiercely contended, amid pursuits and fierce mock battles, for the trophy of a decapitated goat, according to the rites of *bouzkachi*, the great equestrian game of the steppes.

But I was unable to enjoy this enchanted life to the end. A violent and pernicious attack of dysentery obliged me to leave my companions. Over paths and tracks, a Jeep took me to Mazar-Y-Sherif, the principal town of the northern provinces. The Afghan Ariana airline extended there.

When the Dakota stopped rolling across the Kabul airfield, I saw, through the cloud of sand raised by the propellers, Hinstin waving to me.

He had seen my name in the Ariana list of passengers, and imagined that some misfortune had precipitated my return. In any case, he had come to meet me.

And not alone. He was accompanied by a bottle of champagne.

It was waiting in the cool of the airfield *chaikhana.* It was opened on the spot.

I really do not know whether the champagne was a sound medicine for my tortured entrails. But after days and days of heat, dust, tea and often stagnant water, this bottle seemed to me an elixir of life.

To appreciate the true savour of that moment, it must be said that throughout Afghan territory Moslem law strictly forbade the manufacture, sale or use of fermented liquors. Foreigners escaped this rigorous rule. They had the right to import alcohol but only in very restricted quantities and on obtaining a licence from the government. And Hinstin, who had only recently come to Kabul, had not yet got one.

'How did you manage it?' I asked him.

'I borrowed against my quota to come from the French nurses at the Ali-Abad hospital.'

He laughed and his eyes shone with happiness at my pleasure.

Hinstin was no longer living in the Hotel Kabul. During our absence, he had found a little house to let. He took me there, gave me his room and his bed, called the best doctor, saw to my diet and nursed me himself.

As a result, I was soon cured. Nevertheless, I continued to occupy his bed and sit at his table. And without hesitation or embarrassment. Without even thanking him. I felt that he experienced as much pleasure at having me under his roof as I did in being his guest. In this total, instinctive exchange, I recognised the virtues of friendship.

Evening after evening, he told me, in fragments, of his life since the war. After being liberated from Buchenwald, he had met a young woman who had come out of Ravensbruck. They had married and had had two boys. But the years of suffering had given him, already by temperament heedless and adventurous, an unbridled, insatiable need for pleasure.

'After so much privation and torture,' he thought, 'nothing is too good, nothing too dear. And to hell with the rest!'

When this feverish crisis was over, Hinstin had nothing left but debts. He remembered his youth, and once again set out to seek his fortune at the end of the world.

He needed courage. He was over fifty. His ordeals in the concentration camp had not left him unaffected. The high altitude of Kabul was bad for his heart if his stay were prolonged.

But this was not the worst of it. In the old days, when he had travelled in the wilds by rivers and deserts, there had been no tender ties to impair his sense of freedom. Now he had a wife and children whom he loved. Separation was a chronic agony. He said nothing about it. But one cannot mistake a friend's unhappiness when, at some incident, some chance recollection, his voice suddenly breaks and the gold of his eyes grows dim.

And Kabul society offered nothing to compensate or even relieve the agonies of his loneliness. Like all little foreign colonies, it was a closed society, immured in its clannish vanities, its boring gossip and its mean quarrels. Hinstin was not the man to put up with it or take part in it.

And Afghanistan's one great, essential gift—travel through the infinite variety of its provinces, its shady bazaars, the valley of the colossal Buddhas, the superb lakes of Band-Y-Amir, the secret gorges of Nuristan, the mosques of Herat or Kandahar—was denied him. His work held him prisoner in Kabul.

That was why there was always a little melancholy mingled with the audacity, the gaiety and heedlessness of his eyes.

The one thing that really helped him to bear it was that he came to France on business twice a year.

I admit that I went to our first meeting in Paris with a certain fear. Would we recover, in so different a climate, each caught in the net of his preoccupations, conventions and personal obligations, the ease, flexibility and pleasure of a friendship formed in escape and freedom?

In such circumstances, I had often known warm and friendly relationships formed in distant lands quickly lose all their substance. Once mutual memories had been exchanged, neither side had any more to say. The same thing happens with a school or army friend of whom one has lost sight for a long time.

But the instant I saw Hinstin again, I knew everything was all right: talk and silence, emotion, gravity and laughter, the past and the present; in short, friendship.

Kabul had merely been the opportunity, the short cut. The circle of splendid mountains, the difficulty of finding alcohol, the caravans of camels in the street, our games of cards while the bells of the *gadis* tinkled, had merely been friendship's chance background. It would have sprung up as strong and as live anywhere else.

During six years, whenever Hinstin came to Paris and I was there, we saw each other almost every day.

In 1961 I had the opportunity of returning to Afghanistan.

Kabul had greatly changed. The Grand Hotel, which had so much disappointed my companions and myself in 1956, had really become a grand hotel. All around were new, blatant buildings of concrete and glass, as everywhere else in the world. The streets were no longer dust but asphalt. You could only find *gadis*, with their bright colours and their bells, in the suburbs of the town. They had been replaced by taxis.

Once again, I was staying with Hinstin, and in his best room. His way of life had also changed. He had a much bigger and better furnished house than the one I had known. It gave on to a large garden; and there was an annex in which Frenchmen passing through or on business were lodged. There were three servants. Nor did he have any difficulties now over wine and spirits.

His office was in one of the new buildings in the centre of the capital. Its appearance, furnishings and staff showed how his business had developed. Hinstin now represented big firms engaged on public works, or producing agricultural machinery, motor-cars and tyres.

During my stay, there was an international exhibition just outside Kabul in a magnificent natural setting. By insistence, determination and imagination, Hinstin had succeeded in erecting a French pavilion among the massive constructions of Russia, China,

America, India and Iran. It was no more than a tent but arranged with perfect taste by experts in decoration, two young women and a young man, whom Hinstin had got from Paris.

No stand was as successful as this one. The police had to be summoned to organise the crowd of spectators and customers. Poor men, with bare feet, bought up the last flagon of scent and the last watch.

The King of Afghanistan and the notabilities walked through the pavilion. The visit was, of course, official. But behind the protocol, one was aware of a sense of friendship. Several ministers said to me: 'The real French ambassador here is Hinstin.'

He, however, maintained unaltered his simplicity, kindness and generosity. Perhaps an increased weariness tended to make him rather breathless, veiled the tone of his voice and darkened the gold of his eyes. The life at Kabul, its altitude, its climate, and the remoteness of his family weighed on him a little more each year. His very success kept him more than ever a prisoner in the capital and deprived him of the treasures Afghanistan had to offer.

Caravans on the great routes, the breath of enchanted valleys, bathing in mountain streams, cliffs that shelter giant Buddhas, the sublime cemeteries of the nomads on the slopes of desert mountains, the liquid staircase of the Band-Y-Amir lakes, where emerald succeeds to sapphire, and onyx to emerald, forts of purple clay, *chaikhanas* open to the lord, the camel-driver and the shepherd—after six years in Afghanistan, Hinstin, owing to his circumstances, was still ignorant of these things.

For my part, being free and in love with this superb country, I came and went unceasingly. On returning, I told of my discoveries. Sometimes, Daniel Schlumberger, head of the French archaeological mission, who doubtless knows and loves Afghanistan better than anyone else and talks of it with rich understanding, intelligence and eloquence, added all the substance of his knowledge to my superficial impressions.

Hinstin listened to our talk as might have done a child. The gold of dreams shone in his eyes.

Shortly before I left for Iran, the King of Afghanistan, Zahir Shah, granted me an audience. It lasted a long time.

The King wanted to tell me himself of the reasons why the Pushtu tribes of Afghanistan—and he was a member of one of them, king-makers—claimed and supported the tribes of the same origin, language, customs and often family which, owing to the artificial line of the frontier, lived in territory attributed to Pakistan.

The existence of this muffled, latent but embittered conflict was not unknown to me. During my first stay in Kabul, ministers, officers, officials, students, merchants and artisans had all told me of this incision into the quick of the body of a people. It was intolerable to them. They felt it as if it were in their own flesh. I had seen the ideal map of free Pushtunistan distributed, its flags flying and its long-haired warriors dancing. I had met on the great routes the splendid caravans which, twice a year, crossed from one country into the other without formalities and without arms.

I knew that beyond the frontier, which had been traced during the British occupation, rebellion was continuously incubating in the fortress villages built like eagles' nests. Tribes periodically rebelled and the Pakistanis had to use aircraft to quell them.

I knew all this. But to hear it from the King himself made the facts and their repercussions assume a singular importance.

'Loyalty, fidelity, fraternal solidarity,' said Zahir Shah.

I felt that the blood-tie could account for a great deal.

This conversation was not confidential. Indeed, I repeated it to Hinstin. A line appeared on his youthful-looking forehead. He said in a low voice, as if talking to himself: 'If relations are broken off, commerce will become difficult, if not impossible. To reach here, all merchandise has to be unloaded at Karachi, and come through Pakistan by rail and road.'

But his anxious expression soon disappeared. Hinstin recovered his smile with its audacity, nonchalance and fatalism. Besides, he was shortly to fly to France.

By rare good fortune, Hinstin's wife had at once become part of our friendship, indeed a natural, indispensable element of it.

Jacqueline had qualities of rectitude and generous warmth, kindness and imagination, of overflowing vitality and lively concern, of courage and modesty, of goodwill and rather rugged simplicity, which are rare in women—and in men also. She bore, too, the indefinable signs of the major, atrocious experience she had undergone, surmounted and surpassed. Hinstin also. But in her they were more clearly visible.

Buchenwald. Ravensbruck.

One evening, after I had returned from Iran, I was present at a scene of which the memory haunts me. A modest flat in the XVème. There were a dozen people at most. Hinstin, his wife, their two boys, and their closest relations. On the table were a few bottles, cakes and sandwiches. To all appearance an ordinary family gathering.

In fact, it was something very different.

Charles Hinstin had been a commander of the Legion of Honour for a long time past for his services in the Resistance. Jacqueline had just been made a *chevalier* of the same order. She could have received it from an illustrious hand in the presence of a numerous and distinguished audience. She had preferred to receive it at home from her husband.

While Hinstin repeated the ritual words, they looked into each other's eyes. There was no vanity or pride in their features which gradually became more lined and hollow under the influence of emotion. Were they each seeing once again the faces of the butchers, the shades of the dead, the hell of the camps?

Ravensbruck. Buchenwald.

The family party resumed its course.

When leaving for Kabul again, Hinstin said to me with satisfaction: 'The state of my business is now such that I can, indeed must, take on an assistant. Next time I'm over here, I shall look out for a capable young man. When he's been trained, I shall spend most of my time in France.'

His absence was surprisingly brief. It lasted only a few weeks.

And yet I had the impression of seeing a changed and hard-hit man. Had I known and liked him less, I might have been taken in by his manner. To all appearance, he was his usual self, gay, friendly, nonchalant. But there was that slight stoop of the shoulders, the voice that seemed suddenly out of tone, the attention that suddenly wandered and a certain mistiness about his gold eyes.

Usually, on his return, I would ask him about the wonderful friends we had in Kabul, the ministers Scherzade and Adalat, who not only called us their brothers but thought it, or whether Kadir, his cook, still liked whisky as much as ever, and he would enjoy telling about them at length. He had adapted himself admirably to the country. Besides, with his dark complexion, his long face and his arched nose, he might easily have been taken for an Afghan, if he had worn the Astrakhan *koula*.

But this time his replies were short and evasive. It was as if he no longer wanted to think of a country and people who were dear to him.

As the days went by, despite his aptitude for laughter and amusement, his child's gift for fun, I realised that he was preoccupied, anxious, almost hunted.

In the end I put it to him.

'You seem worried,' I said.

'Yes,' he replied.

'Is it serious?'

'To say the least...'

He looked at me with his dull, veiled eyes and went on: 'Do you remember the conversation you had with the King? Well, diplomatic and commercial relations with Pakistan have been broken off for two months. No goods are reaching Afghanistan. Nothing. And, on the basis of success, I've taken a large view. I'm in up to the hilt. If the situation lasts—as it threatens to do—things will be difficult...'

'What then?' I asked.

He felt the anxiety in my voice. It had the effect of dissipating his own. His eyes became light and friendly again.

'Don't think about it any more. There's nothing you can do,' he said. 'I'll come through again. Why shouldn't I?'

After this conversation, Hinstin never allowed me to refer to his difficulties again. He did even better. He led me to believe by his manner that he had resolved or overcome them.

But one evening when we were due to meet, he didn't turn up. I telephoned the Paris firm with which he had connections.

'He left for Kabul by air this morning,' a secretary said.

'But...' I said. 'So quickly... without warning...'

The click of the receiver being replaced was the only answer.

Then one morning Jacqueline telephoned me. She wanted to see me at once. There was disaster in her voice. It was not a presentiment I had, but a certainty. Her face confirmed it. When she said it,

I was ready. She had received a cable. Hinstin's servants had found his lifeless body in his room.

I could not bear to look into Jacqueline's eyes. I lowered mine. I saw her red ribbon and remembered the evening party at which he had given it to her. I could find nothing to say.

As a man grows older, he has increasing difficulty in making a real friendship, even if he wants to, desires it, has an essential need for it. The obligations and burdens the years accumulate erode the availability of time and heart. The critical sense is more acute, intolerance sharper, and weariness supervenes. Generous curiosity and the faculty of welcoming become blunted.

I know, for my part, that when I had turned fifty I thought I had done for ever with that wonderful period when, during the course of a night, a noble and lively relationship could develop between one unknown and another and last for life, when talking and listening were a fecund joy, and laughing, and being moved, and drinking and fighting together against the whole world.

This is why I consider it an extraordinary piece of good fortune that, ten years later, in distant Kabul, I should have acquired once again that gift of youth: a friend.

I very much fear it will be the last milestone on the path of life.

As time passes, the sense of the void left by his death merely increases. But I neither saw his dead face, nor touched his cold body. As a result, I instinctively only half believe it.

And I dream that a *zombie* is walking beneath the sky of that Afghanistan we both loved so much. A *zombie* with gold eyes.